REVIEWING A BUSINESS:
AN INTRODUCTION FOR AGRICULTUR

C000126623

CONTENTS

1.	**Introduction – The Coming Challenge**	3
2.	**The Value of Business Accounts**	5
	2.1 Introduction	
	2.2 Good Businesses Do Not Just Have Accounts, They Use Them	5
	2.3 The Range of Performance between Farming Businesses	5
	2.4 Hallmarks of the Better Farm Businesses	6
3.	**Identify the Business**	8
	3.1 Introduction	8
	3.2 Sole Trader	8
	3.3 Partnership	8
	3.4 Companies	9
	3.5 What is the Real Position?	10
	3.6 Remuneration of the Business Owners	11
4.	**Accounts**	12
	4.1 Introduction	12
	4.2 Accounts	12
	4.3 Accounting Standards	12
	4.4 Accounting Periods	14
	4.5 Matching Expenditure to Income	14
	4.6 Revenue or Capital?	15
	4.7 Comparison	16
	4.8 The Structure of the Profit and Loss Account	16
	4.9 The Structure of the Balance Sheet	17
	4.10 The Structure of a Flow of Funds Statement	17
	4.11 The Notes to the Accounts	18
	4.12 Taxation Accounts	18
	4.13 Partnership Accounts	19
	4.14 Accounts for Joint Ventures	20
	4.15 Digital Accounting	20
5.	**Accounts, Plans and Budgets as Management Tools**	21
	5.1 Introduction	21
	5.2 Looking Ahead: The Business Plan	21
	5.3 Budgets	22
	5.4 Cash Flow	22
	5.5 Management Accounts	23
	5.6 Farm Management Accounting	23
	5.7 Servicing Debt	25
	5.8 Reviewing Business or Investment Proposals	26
6.	**Analysis of Accounts: "Making the Accounts Talk"**	29
	6.1 Introduction	29
	6.2 Measures of Income in Farm Accounting	29
	6.3 EBITDA	31
	6.4 Sensitivity Analysis	31
	6.5 Accounting Ratios	31
7.	**Benchmarking and Other Information – "Measure, Manage, Monitor"**	34
	7.1 Use of Performance Indicators	34
	7.2 Benchmarking	35

	7.3	Accounting Benchmarks	35
	7.4	Physical Benchmarks	36
	7.5	Reviewing Markets	37
	7.6	Other Information	37
8.	**Finance**		39
	8.1	Where Might Money Come From?	39
	8.2	Conventional Lending	40
	8.3	Innovative Funding/Investment	42
	8.4	Crowdfunding	43
	8.5	Peer to Peer Lending	44
9.	**The Growing Need to see Business Value**		46
10.	**Approaches to Valuing a Business**		49
	10.1	Approaches to Valuing a Business	49
	10.2	The Importance of Liquidity	51
	10.3	Static Approaches	51
	10.4	Dynamic Approaches	53
	10.5	Review	55
11.	**Valuing Partnerships, Businesses and Shares**		56
	11.1	Valuation and Partnerships	56
	11.2	Consideration of Partnerships	56
	11.3	What is in the Business? – Warnings from Partnerships	57
	11.4	Shares in a Business	58
	11.5	What is a "Share" in Partnership?	59
	11.6	Valuation of Shares in a Partnership	59
	11.7	Valuation of Shares in a Company	60
	11.8	Issues of Valuation for Businesses in Divorce Cases	62
	11.9	Illustrations from Compulsory Purchase	67
12.	**Reviewing a Farm or Estate Business**		71
	12.1	Background	71
	12.2	Conversations to Come	72
	12.3	The Factors of Production	73
	12.4	Environmental Options	73
	12.5	Sustainability and Resilience	75
	12.6	Information Gathering and Preliminary Review	75
	12.7	Look at Cash Flow	77
	12.8	Looking Ahead	77
	12.9	Beginning the Change and Considering Options	77
	1210	Reviewing the People Involved	80
	12.11	Succession	81
	12.12	Housing	83
13.	**Facilitating Discussion – Helping People Find the Answers**		84
	13.1	Introduction	84
	13.2	A Possible Structure of Issues for Review	84
	13.3	Acting as a Facilitator	85
	13.4	Moving to a Facilitator from Outside the Business	85
	13.5	Approaching the Discussion	85
	13.6	The Opening Meeting for a Family Conversation	86
	13.7	The Facilitator's Roles	87
	13.8	The Outcome and Thereafter	88
Appendix: Schedule of Cases			90

1. Introduction – The Coming Challenge

"It is not the strongest of the species that survives, nor the most intelligent that survives. It is the one that is most adaptable to change."

Attributed to Charles Darwin but he did not say this
Derived from Leon Megginson, Southwestern Social Science Association Journal,1963
However, its success as a quotation is testimony to evolution

1.1 The pressures on farm businesses are expected to accelerate following Brexit, with changes in both the trading environment and domestic policies after the CAP, including the reduction and, in England and Wales, the removal of BPS with the scale of the financial margin it brings to the great majority of farms. Good management will be critical to the ways in which farmers will navigate the next few years and achieve the productivity, innovation or changed approaches that appear required. Moreover, the new policies may require farming businesses to have been reviewed for their sustainability in both business and environmental terms. That is expressly proposed in the 2019 Welsh consultation, *Sustainable Farming and our Land*, as a precondition for entry into the post-Brexit Sustainable Farming Scheme. Aside from such scheme requirements, the economic pressures for change are going to require many businesses to review their position so that they can navigate this period successfully; much of that will turn on sound analysis and good advice.

1.2 Farm accounting has been a discipline since at least the 1960s and accounts have long been a necessary regulatory matter for taxation and loans. Good businesses and businesses under pressure have both made more positive use of accounts, budgets and now increasingly benchmarking to monitor and plan the direction of the business, driving understanding and efficiency and aiding accountability within and by the business.

1.3 As the general national challenge of agricultural productivity is simply the sum of the performance of all the individual businesses, the subjects covered in this paper concern key tools for tackling the much larger picture we face, focussing on improved analysis, understanding and management.

1.4 These skills will also be needed in advising on the prospective post-Brexit government schemes, such as the Environmental Land Management Scheme in England and the Sustainable Farming Scheme in Wales, as well as the potential for private sector initiatives for climate change mitigation, bio-diversity and other environmental goals. Would it be worthwhile for the business to accept their opportunities with their terms, obligations and payment rates? What would aid and complement improved productivity on the farm rather than hinder it?

1.5 The operation of joint ventures such as partnerships, contract farming or other ways of working between farmers, and between farmers and landowners, will usually depend on having and also understanding accounting procedures.

1.6 Many farms and estates will already be involved in or considering a wide range of enterprises beyond food production, whether:
- for direct operation within or alongside the business from processing produce and renewable energy to tourism and retail operations
- by potential business partners or tenants.

1.7   That growing diversity and complexity of clients' businesses and the increasing complications from their interactions with external regimes, such as taxation, with their effects on cash flow add to the challenge, require the intelligent use of accounts and other data in helping each business move forward.

1.8   Much of this may involve a shift in approach for some clients from accounts as an obligation to accounting as a tool for management and planning; for some that will be a move from a focus on gross income and cash flow (if not just the current bank balance) to one on margin and profit – in all, a move from looking at the top line of the accounts to focusing on the bottom line. Of itself, that will drive change but it should be informed change with good decision making.

1.9   This paper is intended to assist agricultural valuers in supporting their clients in managing this change. Having, understanding and using accounts offers the key to the successful management and strategic review of clients' businesses. In setting out where the business has been, they provide a platform of information from which to review where the business and the people in it might be going or could go; planning its future direction and so managing change rather than being managed by it. Alongside the potential of benchmarking for many businesses, accounts can be used to develop an understanding of a business, its strengths and vulnerabilities, where major risks might lie and where it might be improved.

1.10   In this, not everything that is of value can be measured and not everything that can be measured has value. That does not diminish the importance and use of accounts, budgeting tools, benchmarking and their analysis. It is simply to point to the complementary importance of practical judgment of people and situations that is intrinsic to the role of the agricultural valuer, informed by the appraisal of data and the testing of data.

1.11   This calls on the strengths of the profession in not only identifying problems but also drawing on a wide range of knowledge and experience, from land tenure and development control to taxation and business management, to find solutions suitable for the people involved, helping plan the future direction of the business.

1.12   Whether considering structural change, succession or other issues, this is essentially about the people running and dependent on the farming or other business, calling on the agricultural valuer's skills in understanding people and situations and the ability:
    – to analyse the business and its operation
    – to formulate and advise on options
    – to facilitate decision making and implementation.

2. The Value of Business Accounts

2.1 Introduction

2.1.1 Business accounting can be seen as a set of tools for understanding the financial state of a business and how it is navigating its path with formal accounts recording its past and budgets projecting its future course, both helping inform its management, owners, lenders and others interested in the business.

2.1.2 At its most basic, business accounting allows an understanding of whether the business:
- is solvent – does it have net worth after liabilities have been deducted from assets?
- is liquid – does it have free cash to meet the demands made of it?
- is making progress or deteriorating, and the issues relevant to either
- is meeting its owners' requirements
- can satisfy the requirement of current or potential lenders both as to the security for a loan and the ability to service the running costs of interest and repayment of the money borrowed (the principal)
- can assure other suppliers of its creditworthiness.

2.1.3 They enable the identification and assessment of risks to the business.

2.1.4 Accounts and related tools will be required:
- to support tax returns
- to understand the business
- to consider the direction of the business and possible changes
- to plan ahead
- to explain the business to owners and lenders
- to support loan applications and review of loan covenants
- to consider proposals for investment or disposal.

2.1.5 They offer a tool for basic accountability within the business, with the opportunity for those involved to consider and question both past and possible actions and their consequences for the business and those in it.

2.1.7 They will also be valuable as evidence in:
- partnership and other business ownership disputes
- resolving Inheritance tax issues
- tenancy succession claims in England and Wales
- preparing for rent reviews
- some planning applications, as for agricultural dwellings.

2.2 Good Businesses Do Not Just Have Accounts, They Use Them

While accounts can simply be seen as a necessary annual chore, a routine exercise and a matter of record, accounts with business plans and budgets can also be viewed positively as an active management tool to support profitability and take business forward. That later approach will be particularly the case where the business has specifically financial objectives, is navigating its way through challenging times, making major changes or meeting responsibilities to others, such as lenders.

2.3 The Range of Performance between Farming Businesses

2.3.1 While much of the discussion of farming economics is naturally based on average expectations, even if adjusted for the farm in question, agricultural valuers will know the reality of the very wide spread of both technical and financial performance between farmers, with wide variations in yield, costs, financial margin and other factors.

2.3.2   True for all sectors and across the United Kingdom, this can be illustrated by these figures from the 2016/17 Farm Business Survey for Crops England which recorded that for combineable cropping ("cereals") farms:

- the average farm overall lost £71 a hectare from farming before moving into surplus with Basic Payment, agri-environment payments and other on-farm income
- the average farm in the top quartile of those farms (so perhaps representing 4,750 farms) had an average positive contribution to their income from agriculture of £208 per hectare, an advantage of £279/ha (£113/acre) over the average
- the average farm in the bottom quartile (again, perhaps representing 4,750 farms) saw its agricultural activity cost it an average of £332 per hectare, falling short of the overall average by £261/hectare (£108/acre).

Thus, the difference in farming margin between the average in the top 25 per cent of cereals farms and the average for the bottom 25 per cent in 2016/17 was £540/hectare (£219/acre).

2.4   Hallmarks of the Better Farm Businesses

2.4.1   An AHDB study in 2017 identified that the top quartile of farm businesses in any sector were the most financially resilient to change, an issue independent of the scale of the business. A subsequent study for the AHDB by Andersons reviewed the factors that distinguish high performing farms. This identified that only 5 per cent of the difference lay in matters outside the farmer's control:

"almost all the determinants of success are down to the individual the decisions made on the farm and how they are implemented."

2.4.2   The study concluded that for commodity production businesses:

"for the industry overall our assessment of factors in order of priority is as follows:
1. Minimise overhead costs
2. Set goals and compile budgets
3. Compare yourself with others and past performance and gather information
4. Understand your market requirements and meet them
5. Give each detail the attention it deserves
6. Have a mindset for change and innovation
7. Continually improve people management
8. Specialise."

(*The Characteristics of High Performing Farms in the United Kingdom* (November 2018).

2.4.3   These factors will be appropriate with variations in their order for many other rural businesses, including the greater diversity of businesses that add value rather than only produce commodities. While making real improvements on these points might, in the context of any one farm business, not appear easy they would be expected to be typical of more than the top quartile in other sectors without the income of BPS.

2.4.4   *The Best British Farmers: What Gives Them the Edge?* points to lower costs being a more significant feature (65 to 90 per cent of higher profits) of profitable commodity farmers than increasing output (10 to 30 per cent) with the observation that:

"Top performers are often marginally better at everything rather than significantly better at anything. Marginal progress on all aspects of the business makes a considerable improvement to the overall figures."

It concluded that:

> "Ultimately though, the success or failure of any business comes down to one variable, the entrepreneur at its helm. Regardless of the support, subsidy, information emails, loans, trade events or research, the talent and drive of the individual to be the "best in class" is the key determinant that turns ordinary into extraordinary." (Andersons report for the Oxford Farming Conference 2015)

2.4.5   Similarly, the report for the Prince's Countryside Fund, *Is There a Future for the Small Family Farm in the UK* (Winter et al, 2016) advised that:

> "Regardless of size the most resilient and successful farm businesses run profitable agricultural enterprises as well as gaining higher than average income from agri-environmental payments and diversification, whilst relying least in proportional terms on the Single Farm Payment (now Basic Payment Scheme). In other words, profitable and successful farm businesses are good at everything they do."

That has underpinned the development of the Fund's Resilience Programme convening groups of farmers in successive areas to review their businesses with the aid of a business health check tool.

3. IDENTIFY THE BUSINESS

3.1   Introduction

Farming businesses are typically partnerships, solely comprising family members, though a significant number are sole traders. Trusts may be found, especially with longer standing families or where there is charity involvement, whether farming in their own right or in a partnership or other relationship. Relatively few are companies, though these are more strongly represented among the larger and more commercial businesses. Some will be structured as limited liability partnerships, typically where commercial liability is seen as an issue, as for processing, a diversification or as a contractor. The business structure may own the land farmed or farm it on a tenancy or licence.

3.2   Sole Trader

The individual operates the business as a personal venture with its assets and liabilities, possibly employing others and instructing others to provide services to it (as with instructing a farming contractor).

3.3   Partnership

3.3.1   Partnerships operates under the Partnerships Act 1890 which applies throughout the United Kingdom and provides very basic default terms that can be overridden or developed by the partnership agreement, making that an important document, where it exists. That Act defines a partnership as:

> "the relation that subsists between persons carrying on a business in common with a view of profit" (s.1(1)).

The critical points in that are:

- more than one person is involved
- they are acting together in a business and so mutual fiduciary duties between them, and each as the agent of the others
- with a view to profit which they then share between them as they may agree.

3.3.2   There need not be a partnership agreement as a partnership can simply arise by the behaviour of the parties. S.2(3) of the Act provides that

> "the receipt by a person of a share of the profits of a business is prima facie evidence that he is a partner in the business, but the receipt of such as share, or of a payment contingent on or varying with the profits of business, does not of itself make him a partner in the business."

3.3.3   The partnership ends when that relationship ends: the partnership is dissolved and the business is wound up. That termination may be:

- under procedures provided by the partnership agreement
- by agreement between the partners
- under a court order
- if not regulated by the agreement, at will by one partner giving notice at any time to the others (or by default under the Act on a partner's death).

3.3.4   Farming partnerships rarely include anyone who is not a family member. Occasionally, a more specialist enterprise may operate as separate partnership and include someone with relevant skills as a partner.

3.3.5   In England, Wales and Northern Ireland, the partnership does not have a legal identity, it being a relationship between persons that do and who are jointly and severally liable for it. Thus, the partnership does not itself enter into contracts, and so, for example, cannot itself be a tenant.

3.3.6   However, under Scottish law a partnership does have its own legal personality and so can be a tenant.

3.3.7   The law has then provided two specific forms of partnership, responding to the problems found with the mutual liability between partners.

3.3.8   Limited Partnerships operate under the Limited Partnerships Act 1907, enabling an agreement to limit a partner's liability to the enterprise but thereby also limiting that partner's management capacity. Thus, the management of the partnership lies with those (commonly, the general partner(s)) who are responsible for its liabilities. In Scotland, this was developed as a means to regulate the length of a secure agricultural tenancy under the Agricultural Holdings (Scotland) Act 1991, whereby a limited partnership would be created to be the tenant – a model used until the 2003 legislation. The landowner or nominee would be a limited partner and the participating farmer the general partner, so with management control and liability. The partnership agreement would define or control the length of the partnership (and so, in Scotland, the legal existence of the tenant).

3.3.9   Limited liability partnerships operate under the Limited Liability Partnerships Act 2000. Largely a response to the difficulties found over liabilities in very large professional partnerships, this Act creates what can be seen as hybrid between a company and a partnership with a partnership structure but also a legal personality allowing the limitation of liability accompanied by some public disclosure to Companies House of accounts but not the partnership deed. In farming, this has been adopted by some, often larger business where public liability might be an issue, as with contracting or processing.

3.4   Companies
3.4.1   These operate under the Companies Act 2006 (including its provisions on liquidation) and having its own legal personality. While companies may also be unlimited or limited by guarantee, companies in business will almost always have limited liability with the corollary of some level of disclosure of accounts, constitution and management to Companies House. Thus, those they trade with accept the potential for risk from limited liability in exchange for some public information about the state of the company.

3.4.2   The company will be owned by its shareholders and managed by its directors. In a small company there may often be close overlap between shareholders and directors, though directors may also include those with management or other expertise and who might not have shares. The shareholders take their return by way of dividends on their shares where this can be paid.

3.4.3   The great majority of the companies that will be met in practice will be private limited companies whose shares are not publicly available but held by a relatively small number of shareholders with the sale or transfer of company shares handled privately.

3.4.4   Other forms of company include:
- **Company limited by guarantee** – Here, the members (rather than shareholders) act as guarantors each being responsible for a typically nominal sum should the company be wound up.
- **Public Company** – This is a company in which anyone can buy shares, being open to the public. A Public Limited Company (PLC) must have allotted shares to the total value of at least £50,000 before it can start business.
- **Community Interest Company** – This form was created for companies created with the intention of using their assets and profits for the good of a community rather than maximising profits for shareholders.

3.4.5 Only a minority of farm businesses operate as companies though these may often be larger or more complex businesses. While the historic pattern saw farmland, buildings and dwellings included when the company was incorporated, that is less the case for more recent companies with the problems found with:
- asset disposal where the receipt is taxed first on the disposal by the company and then on any return of that value to the shareholders
- benefits in kind for directors, as with the occupation of farmhouses.

3.4.6 A company structure is one of the forms used where farmers combine their farming operations to seek more efficient use of resources, giving the company access to their land for farming purposes but nothing more than that.

3.4.7 In each case, the assets, such as farm property or livestock, are likely to have value as such. Where, as perhaps with a farm diversification or an added value enterprise, there is the opportunity to sell the access to profit to someone else that goodwill may have a value. However, where the hope of profit stems only from the individual's labour and management, that is less likely to be possible.

3.5 What is the Real Position?

3.5.1 While may usually be clear what the business is and who owns it, there are occasions when it can sometimes be harder than might be imagined to determine the actual identity of the business, especially where a family has been farming in a variety of ways, often informal, for many years. It may be particularly important to identify which assets are owned by the business and which by other individuals, however closely related.

3.5.2 Where it may appear that there is a single farmer who may in reality be the guiding force in the overall business, there may also be a partnership but also various ownerships, potentially including trusts, and perhaps companies with interlocking interactions and sometimes some haziness about which assets lie where and what is paid for them. That can become more complex where, perhaps for later convenience, they are treated as having moved between entities with the true legal structure no longer recalled or understood. Business entities may have been established for a purpose many years ago and have then been forgotten as participants, needs, knowledge or interests have changed, making it hard to construct an accurate analysis of the position. Where there has been no need to look at a tenancy agreement for many years, the identity of the actual tenants may not be to the front of the minds of those now involved.

3.5.3 This may also apply to accounting as where several operations (perhaps including a farm contracting relationship) are run through a single account, needing to be disaggregated to gain a clear understanding of the various activities.

3.5.4 These issues apply not only for business analysis but also where there is a farm sale or the property becomes subject to compulsory purchase when relevant interests have to be identified. In particular, HS2 has questioned situations where there is either no partnership agreement, an inadequate one or the landowner is not part of the farming business, suggesting that unless the landowner and the farming business are the same or the business has some interest in the land then it will not pay compensation for business losses.

3.5.5 In particular and as explored below, farming partnership accounts are often a poor source of evidence about assets, relationships and liabilities, only tested where a family dispute heads for litigation.

3.5.6 Where such a situation is met, it is worth spending early time in gaining as clear a picture as possible of the interests and entities in play rather than being surprised later.

If this can be accurately clarified in the instruction to the valuer and tested and confirmed in an early meeting, it will assist the process considerably. This will help understand who the client is and whether there are any conflicts of interest. There may be circumstances where some interests require separate advice and representation.

3.5.7   Further, companies and limited liability partnerships are now required to declare to Companies House the identity of Persons with Significant Control (PSCs) whether or not they are actually shareholders, partners or directors.

3.6   Remuneration of the Business Owners

3.6.1   The different business structures see the business owners remunerated in different ways, potentially affecting the impression that the accounts might give.

3.6.2   For **sole traders and partnerships**, the business owner's reward is the profit left after properly allocated costs have been set against income. If the owners are not to draw from the business, then their income is "below the line". What they do not take from that profit is available for reinvestment or simply as a financial cushion for the business, helping handle risk and volatility. The business owners will have to make their own provision for retirement pensions from their profits, not as a cost of the business.

3.6.3   Where such a business is being reviewed for purchase into a company the future liability for salaries for those doing the work that had been done by the sole trader or partners needs to be considered.

3.6.4   Where the business is a **company**, it is a legal entity in its own right and its finances can be seen as ring-fenced from those involved in it. The company will be assessed to Corporation Tax on its profits in its own right, with rates lower than those generally applying for Income Tax but and further reduced form small companies. That will include any gains made on the sale of property or other assets on which an individual would be liable to Capital Gains Tax.

3.6.5   Directors and others working for it can draw salaries (or have other remuneration such as pension provision) and these will be a cost of the business, reducing its profit (or increasing its loss). Their income in that capacity is "above the line"; that is, before reporting profit and loss. Their business income will be assessed to Income Tax as trading income. In assessing a company's accounts, it might be necessary to consider if the payments to directors reflect the market and the company's fortunes, or are unreasonably high or atypically low.

3.6.6   The business owners will be the shareholders. They are entitled to appoint the directors and, in a small family company, will often be some or all of the directors, potentially drawing a salary in that capacity which will be assessed to Income Tax as employment earnings through PAYE. Where directors have benefits in kind, such as housing, that will be liable to assessment for tax (see, for example, the relevant sections of the CAAV publication, *Taxation of Rural Dwellings*).

3.6.7   However, the remuneration for shareholders comes from the potential distribution of income from the company through dividends paid on the shares. Those payments are money paid out of the company to its owners, normally but not necessarily out of profits not needed for the future of the business. As investment income, dividends are generally taxed at lower rates of Income Tax (though this difference has been narrowing), are not liable for National Insurance but are not relevant to pension contributions. Thus, if a company chooses to distribute profits from a capital gain to its shareholders, that gain will have been taxed as company income and then again as income in the hands of its shareholders.

4. ACCOUNTS

4.1   Introduction

Accounting processes are not only used to record the past and meet legal obligations for taxation and, for companies and limited liability partnerships, Companies House but also:

– as part of the process of current management and accountability of the business both internally and to those with claims on it, such as lenders

– to look ahead to plan and help the development of the business.

The opening sections of this chapter set out the approach to accounts for small companies as this will, in general, offer a structure for understanding the accounts of unincorporated businesses, albeit that they are not typically subject to the same level of regulation.

4.2   Accounts

4.2.1   The formal accounts, attested by a third party professional (almost always an accountant), report on the business' financial performance in the stated accounting period, typically a year. They will do this with:

– a balance sheet recording the stated values of the business' assets and liabilities at the opening and closing of that accounting period

– the profit and loss account showing the income and expenditure of the business in that period

– for some accounts, a flow of funds statement showing movements in overall values including fixed assets

– accompanying explanatory notes

– a declaration by the third party that the accounts represent a true and fair record of the position and a statement as to whether the business is a going concern.

4.2.2   The accounts will be expected to have been prepared following recognised accounting standards which set out the requirements and norms for businesses by their size, ownership structure and nature.

4.2.3   The structure of the accounts may be dictated by the structure of the business, such as whether it is a partnership, a limited liability partnership, a company, a charity or in some other form.

4.2.4   Thus, each set of accounts is a historic record of the business, a retrospective report on its performance following decisions taken in the past. They offer a snapshot of its financial position at the beginning and the end of the year and an account of its income and expenditure between those dates, with comparative figures from the previous account period. For a company, directors are required to advise of any post-balance events between the closing date and the date when the accounts were settled.

4.2.5   Their current relevance may be limited by their retrospective nature as a record of a year that will have had its own circumstances but, in many cases, they may offer the best evidence to hand.

4.3   Accounting Standards

4.3.1   The recognised standards for the preparation of financial accounts are now set out in Financial Reporting Standards (FRS) 100 to 105. Applying to annual accounts in the United Kingdom and the Republic of Ireland, FRS govern the preparation of accounts and their presentation including the disclosures made in them.

4.3.2   Strictly, FRS are only mandatory for companies but, in practice, they set the standards used for business accounts more generally.

4.3.3   These generally work from the concept of "fair value", here as an accountancy concept, defined for these purposes by International Financial Reporting Standards as:
"The price that would be received to sell an asset or paid to transfer a liability in an orderly transaction between market participants at the measurement date" (International Accounting Standards Board (IASB), International Financial Reporting Standards (IFRS) 13, paragraph 1).

4.3.4   The relevant standards depend on the size of the business, as assessed using EU business size classifications. FRS 102 applies to "small entities" and FRS 105 can apply to "micro-entities". More demanding standards apply to larger businesses but most agricultural valuers might usually meet only few of these.

4.3.5   A "small entity" is one that meets two of three tests, most recently defined as:
– a balance sheet as stated in the accounts (but gross before liabilities) of under £5.1 million
– a turnover under £10.2 million
– fewer than 50 employees.

4.3.6   "Micro-entities", which can adopt separate rules, are defined as those that meet two of three tests
– a balance sheet as stated in the accounts (but gross before liabilities) of under £316,000
– a turnover under £632,000
– fewer than 10 employees.

4.3.7   **FRS 102**, with its 350 pages, is the significant standard for most businesses. Within that, the new standards for "small entities" are set out at Section 1A (replacing FRSSE 2008 and, where it was adopted, FRSSE 2015). Its complete text can be seen at: https://www.frc.org.uk/Our-Work/Publications/Accounting-and-Reporting-Policy/FRS-102-The-Financial-Reporting-Standard-applicab.pdf

4.3.8   The practical application in agricultural contexts of this apparent move to fair value from the traditional and prudent basis of the lower of cost or net realisable value is discussed in Section 4 of *Guidance Notes on Agricultural Stock Valuations for Tax Purposes*, Third Edition, Numbered Publication 210 (June 2012). In summary, under FRS 102:
– the stocktaking can continue to be on the lower of cost and net realisable value
– all animals may have to be included in the stocktaking, with production animals now to be in the stocktaking and then taken out in the tax adjustment by the accountant
– the business can opt to move to a fair value but having done so cannot then opt back
– the longstanding provision for using deemed costs are not altered by FRS 102 which still expects that production costs should be used where they are available. Having real production costs to hand will be more useful in analysing the business.

4.3.9   Government grants and subsidies (so including Basic Payment, other direct payments and agri-environment agreement payments) can be considered on one of two bases:
– performance – when all conditions for the payment are met
– accruals – applied proportionately to the accountancy period(s) to which it is relevant once the payment is recognised.
Any capital grants, as perhaps under Countryside Stewardship, are to be released in full to the profit and loss account, rather than released over the life of the asset.

4.3.10   Intangibles (other than goodwill) may be measured after initial recognition using either:

- the cost model under which assets are recognised at cost less accumulated amortisation, or
- the revaluation model which measures them at fair value at the date of revaluation less subsequent amortisation and impairment losses. Revaluation is only possible when fair value can be determined by reference to an active market for an intangible.

Intangibles and goodwill are considered to have a finite useful life and so should be amortised systematically over their life. If it is not possible to make a reliable estimate of the useful life, it should be deemed not to exceed 5 years.

4.3.11   **FRS 105** – While this standard offers a separate approach for "micro-entities", many prefer to use FRS102, partly to avoid issues where a business moves over the boundary into being a small entity, perhaps only because of an increase in grain prices or land values. FRS105 is also seen as very prescriptive, requiring disclosure in particular ways.

4.3.12   Fixed assets are to be recorded at cost and may not be revalued. That would affect a business that had re-valued land on its balance sheet as it would now have to revert to the cost basis.

4.3.13   Stocks are to be valued at the lesser of cost and net realisable value; fair value accounting is not permitted.

4.3.14   **Larger Businesses** – Larger businesses are required to use fair value and so more clearly follow the wording of International Accounting Standard (IAS) 41 on agriculture with concepts such as biological assets. Where a business moves to this basis, then the preceding accounts need to be restated on the new basis.

4.3.15   **Charity Accounts** – Accounting standards provide a specific framework for accountants to set out the accounts of charities: SORP, the Statement of Recognised Practice under Financial Reporting Standard 102.

4.4   Accounting Periods

4.4.1   The accounts report financial performance over a stated period of time. While the initial period may be for a period of months and reasons may arise for the chosen period to change, this will normally be a year to a conventional date consistent over the life of the business.

This may often be to March 31st (so just before the end of the tax year). Many arable businesses run to a September 30th year end. There may be business reasons – here the completion of a conventional arable production cycle – to choose a particular year end. Some may be on a calendar year basis, to December 31st.

4.4.2   It may be awkward to have an accounting year that does not match the pattern of VAT quarters, making it a matter of choice as to which changes in the event of any mismatch.

4.5   Matching Expenditure to Income

4.5.1   Most accounts will be prepared on an **accruals** rather than a cash flow basis. While a cash flow basis simply records when payments move in or out of the business, the accruals basis:

- recognises accounts as at the date when they are become due
- adjusts them for the period to which they relate with whether as prepayments or accruals at the start and end of the accounting year.

Example – An insurance policy is taken out for a year from September 30th when the accounting period runs to March 31st. Half that payment will be allocated to the year in question as half of its value lies in that year but the other half of the payment is held over to the following year as the payment also provides a service for the first half of that year.

4.5.2   Where expenditure in one year is towards income in another year, that is handled through **stocktaking** which holds such costs over to the year in which the income will arise so that they are matched with each other. This will be an issue for most businesses.

4.5.3   The point can be illustrated by the case of an Easter egg manufacturer with a March 30th year end. In some years, Easter may be early and be within the same year as the eggs are made with the associated spending on materials; in others it may be in the following accounting year. If treated simply in cash flow terms, the accounts could show large swings between years despite an unchanged performance, simply because of the varying date of Easter. The resulting accounts would then be misleading. Where Easter is before the March 30th year end, cost is anyway matched against income. Where it is in the following year, those costs of the eggs to be sold are identified and carried to that year so it can be put against the income for which they were spent.

4.5.4   For an arable farm with a September 30th year end, stocks to be carried forward against income in the following year will include both:
  – harvested grain held in store for sale after September 30th
  – growing crops already sown by then.

4.5.5   For a full account of agricultural stocktaking with its specific issues and rules, see the CAAV publication No.201, *Guidance Notes on Agricultural Stock Valuations for Tax Purposes*.

4.6   Revenue or Capital?

4.6.1   One critical issue for accounting (and also taxation) is whether items of expenditure are treated as capital or as revenue.

4.6.2   Revenue items are current spending and directly allocated to the profit and loss account, sometimes through the medium of the stocktaking where they are to be matched against future sales. For tax accounts they are allowable expenses for Income Tax or Corporation Tax.

4.6.3   Capital items are new investment in the business, such as buildings, land improvements, plant and machinery, yielding benefits over time which are reflected in the profit and loss account only through their depreciation (and in taxation accounts only through capital allowances).

4.6.4   While the distinction may appear clear, in practice there are areas where this is a matter of judgment. That is particularly so where work includes elements of both renewal and improvement, sometimes to meet modern standards. HMRC's Business Income Manual describes a repair as something which "restores the asset to what it originally had been". However, many works will also include an element of improvement.

4.6.5   Distinguishing between a repair and a replacement turns on what work is being done. Thus, if the work is to a part of building, it may well be a repair of that building than a replacement of that part.

4.6.6   Thus, a like-for-like rewiring of a farmhouse would be a repair of the farmhouse; adding a new electrical system would be an improvement. It is recognised that modern standards could require new features in an electrical system; where this is the case it would still be accepted as repair. That point has long been tested by the replacement of single glazed windows with double glazed ones.

4.6.7   In addition to long standing case law in this area, a Tribunal case, *G Pratt and Sons v HMRC* reviewed the resurfacing of a farm drive. Referring to the classic property law decision, *Lurcot v Wakely* in which it was said that:

> ""Repair" is restoration by renewal or replacement of subordinate parts of a whole. Renewal as distinguished from repair is reconstruction of the entirety, meaning by the entirety not necessarily, but substantially, the whole subject matter under discussion."

the Tribunal determined that:

> "the work on the farm drive consisted of a new concrete surface being placed over the existing tarmac which had been broken up to form a hard-core base. There was not, in our judgment, a renewal of the entirety of the drive, or the part of the yard in which the concrete was replaced, but a repair to an existing asset. We may have taken a different view if the drive had been altered to accommodate larger milk tankers or to allow access for larger lorries bringing farm supplies but it was not. Before the work on the drive the dairy sent 20,000 litre tankers for milk collections and they continued to do so following its completion, the same applies to deliveries by suppliers to the farm."

4.6.8   Where this issue becomes relevant in appraising accounts, the fixed asset register supporting the accounts may help answer questions.

4.7   Comparison

4.7.1   Accounts conventionally show the previous year's equivalent figures alongside both the Profit and Loss Account and the Balance Sheet. That gives an immediate basis for comparison and so initial questions. A more thorough review would look at several years' figures – conventionally three, as earlier accounts can be too distant and too much may have changed for useful comparison – together with an account of the evolution of the business.

4.7.2   With the variations between businesses, external comparison and benchmarking will more usually be of comparative unit costs, percentages (as for gross margin) and ratios derived from the accounts for each business. Some of the tools for doing this are in Chapter 5.

4.8   The Structure of the Profit and Loss Account

NB For a charity or not for profit body, this will be the Income and Expenditure Account
This records the income and expenditure of the business over the accounting period.

4.8.1   These sums are conventionally recorded excluding VAT. Where, as with businesses that are partially exempt from VAT, some VAT that cannot be recovered that is recorded as an item of expenditure in its own right.

4.8.2   Income is set out first to give gross turnover, usually broken down by a number of headings and then totalled, with adjustments for opening and closing values for the accounting period.

4.8.3   Expenditure is set out next, broken down by a number of headings and then totalled. Farming accounts may see these set out in the two categories of direct costs and overheads though ultimately the tax returns will require figures by specified headings.

4.8.4   Elements of un-reimbursed private benefit to the business owners or directors should be excluded. That might include private use of a car or of a dwelling.

4.8.5   Items of capital expenditure, whether as new investment or improvement of existing assets, should be excluded. Their annual input to the business will be recorded in the assessment of depreciation.

4.9   The Structure of the Balance Sheet

4.9.1   The balance sheet sets out the assets of the business and then its liabilities with the net balance being the reserves.

4.9.2   The assets will usually be shown as:
– **fixed assets** and so:
  ○ **tangible assets** such as land and buildings, plant, machinery and equipment
  ○ **intangible assets** such as investments
– **current assets**, such as:
  ○ **stocks** – goods held to be sold, such as grain in store, growing crops, livestock, consumable goods in such as fertilisers, and forage in store for feeding
  ○ **debtors** – money owed to the business. For a farm this could include a VAT refund as much as sales income awaited. It can also include prepayments by the business for something in a later accounting period.
  ○ **Cash.**

4.9.3   Creditors, those to whom the business owes money, are typically considered as to whether the liability is due within a year of the balance sheet date or on longer term basis.

4.9.4   Those failing due within a year, as will be the case for most goods and services bought by a business but not yet paid for, are its **current liabilities.** These also include bank overdrafts, merchant credit and hire purchase commitments.

4.9.5   These current liabilities are subtracted from current assets to give **net current assets**. If this value is negative, the business may well have a liquidity problem.

4.9.6   The balance sheet will then add the value of fixed assets and the net current assets to give **total assets less current liabilities**. If this value is negative, the business is very likely to have a solvency problem.

4.9.7   Longer term liabilities are then considered, such as mortgages and also provisions such as for taxation, to give **net assets,** also known as **reserves** (or **net worth**). That is where the balance sheet balances.

4.10   The Structure of a Flow of Funds Statement (or Cash Flow Statement)

4.10.1   Where provided, this gives a statement of how funds have increased or decreased over the accounting period, with the sources and applications of those movements as they affect working capital. As such, it can give useful information helping to understand:
– if an increase in funds has come from a sale of assets or an improvement in the business's performance
– why a business is making a loss despite being financially sound or vice versa
– whether short term sources of funds are being used to create long term investment or the reverse.

4.10.2 It will show:
- the net cash generated from or provided to the operating business
- the net cash generated from or provided to other activities, such as
  ○ the purchase of assets, tangible, fixed and intangible
  ○ the sale of assets, tangible, fixed and intangible
  ○ interest paid or received
  ○ dividends received or paid

4.10.3 The resulting total for net cash movement is then added to the opening position for cash and cash equivalents at the start of the year to give a closing position at its end.

4.11   The Notes to the Accounts

A formal set of annual accounts will typically have a set of notes, cross referred to particular figures, which may:
- explain accounting policies, such as those for depreciation, and cover compliance and administrative points, and
- give more detail on specific points, such as a breakdown of debtors.

4.12   Taxation Accounts

4.12.1 One prime purpose for accounts is to support the tax returns for the individuals who own the business (Income Tax) or the company that is the business (Corporation Tax).

4.12.2 With their statutory framework, they can be more historic than might be assumed, more than the ordinary lags in preparing accounts:
- Income Tax returns for income in a year to 5th April have to be made by January 31st in the year following. The relevant farm accounts would be those running to a year end date (balance sheet date) in that tax year. Thus, a set of arable accounts for the year form 1st October 2018 to September 30th 2019 will be part of a tax return to be made by January 31st 2021
- Corporation Tax returns are to be made within ten months of the year end (and accounts are to be submitted to Companies House within nine months of the year end).

4.12.3 Business accounts are likely to have to be adjusted for use with taxation returns, following the requirements of the law. The law generally expects accounts for taxation purposes to be prepared in accordance with conventional accounting practice but then intervenes to require specific adjustments.

4.12.4 The principal adjustments relevant to farming accounts are:
- the replacement of depreciation of capital investment with capital allowances
- the rules of the herd basis for any production animals where this has been adopted
- for private use of business assets.

4.12.5 Individuals may also take advantage of the rules for two or five year averaging of profits, with some potential complexity when viewing a partnership where different people may take different options.

4.12.6 There may also be a need to adjust the breakdown from the headings that are useful to the owners and managers of the business to those required for the tax return.

4.12.10 Reconstituting Accounts – Where it proves that taxation accounts are the only accounts that are available, then those adjustments need to be unwound to re-create the accounts as they would be prepared on a conventional basis.

4.13   Partnership Accounts

4.13.1   Typically similar to accounts for a sole trader, partnership accounts are also generally prepared for the reference of the business owners (here the partners), taxation purposes and for lenders.

4.13.2   Ordinary partnerships are not subject to the guidelines of the Companies Act and, as unincorporated businesses, are outside the Financial Reporting Standards, though they might follow them in substance.

4.13.3   Very few partnership accounts are audited and the expectation of an external accountant is more in the nature of reviewing their reliability and not to give an opinion as to whether the show a true and fair view. That may mean that if important questions arise over the accuracy of the accounts, further work may be needed to understand the position. A further consequence is that there will be less consistency between partnership accounts than between company accounts, potentially making financial benchmarking harder.

4.13.4   However, the limitation of liability for a limited liability partnership brings greater disclosure. That sees the accounts obliged to show a true and fair view, follow a standard format as for companies and include detailed notes, all lodged with Companies House. However, LLPs qualifying as small entities need not be audited.

4.13.5   All partners have the right to inspect the partnership books and accounts (Partnership Act s.24(9)).

4.13.6   While having a balance sheet and a profit and loss account, they should also include a capital account for each partner, recording the introduction and withdrawal of capital by each partner, and so how much capital each partner has invested in the business.

4.13.7   There may also be a record of the current account for each partner, recoding cash withdrawn and profits allocated. Profits that the partner has not drawn down at the end of the accounting period might be carried forward as such or transferred to that partner's capital account. In some smaller partnerships, the current account can be combined with the capital account as a single capital account.

4.13.8   With the structure of a partnership being a business relationship for profit, partnership accounts should show how profits and losses in any accounting period are divided between the partners. The basis for that should be in the partnership agreement, thought the Act provides for equal shares as a default. In some cases, the agreement may provide for a set sum to be paid to a partner for a commitment to the business (as if it were a salary – but "salaried partners" might be employees chargeable to the profit and loss account, not actual partners). It could also be that partners are credited with interest (typically at a rate specified in the agreement) on their capital, so with differing rewards for different levels of investment.

4.13.9   Unlike a sole trader, the partnership is not taxable in its own right (albeit being required to make a tax return). Each partner is liable to taxation on their share of the partnership profit along with any other taxable income they may have.

4.13.10 Where the partnership account is used to pay the partners' tax liabilities that should be shown as a charge against the relevant partners' current accounts. Where that would see the current account overdrawn, the accounts might instead show a separate provision for Income Tax.

4.13.11 There might also be provision for deferred tax liabilities, as where income is recognised in one period but taxed in another one.

4.14 Accounts for Joint Ventures

4.14.1 Some arrangements for joint ventures between landowners and farmers or between farmers are specifically structured as separate businesses, whether partnerships or jointly owned companies, and so have their own accounts.

4.14.2 Other forms of joint venture, such as contract farming or the possible forms of share farming, conventionally:
- require the keeping of separate accounts and records for the venture
- use a separate bank account, usually in joint names and often referred to as a No.2 account

isolating the operation of the venture from the other businesses of the parties to give clarity and accountability to it.

4.14.3 Where this is not done, the position can easily become confused to the disadvantage of at least one, if not all, parties. An apparent saving in bookkeeping costs can result in greater accountancy costs while ensuring the correct allocation of any VAT recovery can become challenging.

4.14.4 Those accounts are just as susceptible to the approaches and analysis reviewed in the next two chapters as are individual farm accounts. Indeed, by making explicit both the success or otherwise of the business and parties' financial claims on it, the actual position of the business may be more obvious.

4.15 Digital Accounting

4.15.1 Accounts for whatever purpose are increasingly kept digitally using systems from spreadsheets within programmes such as Excel to dedicated software such as Sage while there are also specialised farm accounting systems.

4.15.2 These developments are given more force by the introduction of HMRC's Making Tax Digital programme, initially for VAT but potentially more widely, requiring electronic interaction by or on behalf of the taxpayer with HMRC on at least a quarterly basis. This requires the software used to be compatible with HMRC's systems – Excel is not understood to be compatible.

4.15.3 As some other jurisdictions are seen to have gone further down this route (even to raising invoices), it is seen as likely to develop further, both easing the costs of HMRC's administration and as a response to the issues around tax avoidance and money laundering.

4.15.4 In whatever way the accounts are kept electronically, it makes it easier to look at them more regularly and in real time as well as to test assumptions and sensitivities to possible changes.

5. ACCOUNTS, PLANS AND BUDGETS AS MANAGEMENT TOOLS

5.1 Introduction

5.1.1 While some clients will see accounting as an annual obligation recording a past that has happened, preferring to judge matters by cash flow or bank balances, it should be used positively to understand the present and prepare for the future.

5.1.2 All attempts to analyse and prepare for the future turn on making assumptions – indeed, with this historic nature of much evidence, that may also be true for assessing the present state of some businesses. The effectiveness of this work turns on the quality of the assumptions that are made.

5.2 Looking Ahead – The Business Plan

5.2.1 This is a review and a description, often for a year but possibly also over a period of years, for the course of the business. Issues in that can include:
- what is the business doing?
- what is it going to do?
- any strategic analysis – as for strengths, weaknesses, opportunities and threats
- lessons from benchmarking and other external reference
- conclusions from that – what problems need to be tackled? What opportunities taken?
- what are the changes to be made? And why?
- what is their justification or return? how are they to be funded?
- the resources of the business
- the liabilities of the business
- people with skills and issues
- leadership and governance
- longer term direction, succession
- resilience and adaptability.

5.2.2 For a conventional farming business, this may work from reviewing markets, income streams and costs, planning the rotation, considering investment and efficiency, to considering soil management and family succession.

5.2.3 One approach is to prepare a "no change" budget, showing how the business might perform if nothing is changed in how it operates. That can provide a basis with which to compare the potential outcomes of possible changes to the business and to test variations in assumptions.

5.2.4 It can help to have an external conversation as the plan develops, such as with an adviser, which can make it easier to look at issues that may be difficult.

5.2.5 Standard figures and benchmarking can be available from the work of the AHDB, costings texts, materials from the agricultural departments of the banks and others. In some areas there may be farmer discussion groups that do this while others may have access to the Prince's Countryside Fund Resilience programme with its business health check.

5.2.6 As the plan comes together, headings such as these may help give it an order and sense of logic to assist its development, external presentation (as to a bank) and future reference:
- what is its objective?
- what is to be output?

- who are the customers?
- who is to deliver it?
- what resources are needed to achieve this?
- what investment needs to be made?
- what is the projected income?
- what are the projected costs?
- what risks are identified for achieving that?

5.2.7 That can then be expressed in the accompanying financial budget which will also allow a means to test for changes in assumptions. It is helpful if that budget is not only for the coming year but also projects forward for the following two years, allowing for the time it may take to make changes and for them to work through as well as testing their cumulative effect.

5.3 Budgets

5.3.1 While accounts are historic records of performance, preparing a budget is a means to plan ahead. It is, in essence, the Business Plan worked through with financial values, giving an arithmetical way of testing and exploring assumptions.

5.3.2 A budget is not a forecast but a projection requiring the business to crystallise, consider and test the assumptions and issues relevant to the accounting period in question. It will only be as good as the assumptions and deductions used are valid while it cannot take account of the unforeseen events that are part of the future. Its value is:
- in producing the projection of those assumptions and deductions as to where the business will go on their basis
- the required knowledge and analysis of the business and its issues required to prepare the budget
- a basis for reviewing performance and managing the business.

5.3.3 The budget may simply be for the whole accounting period. While that may be needed for use with a lender or for comparing with the accounts, it might be of more use for real analysis if it is were also (or alternatively) prepared across the typical production cycle for the main enterprises on the farm which might not match the accounting period or even be for a year, with a range from rearing heifers to growing lettuce.

5.3.4 The budget could also be sub-divided by months or quarters, according to the nature and demands of the business, but this is more likely to be relevant to the subsequent cash flow.

5.3.5 It can help to test the assumptions and deductions by projecting them over the following year or two. This may test and highlight issues more clearly than a single accounting period.

5.3.5 That can also test whether the approach to the budget has been cautious, prudent, realistic or optimistic, especially as unexpected events tend to be adverse and adverse events tend to be more testing of a business.

5.3.6 The budget process inter-relates with both cash flow projection and management accounts.

5.4 Cash Flow

5.4.1 Even where a business is profitable across a whole accounting period, it may not be generating the free cash to meet its financial obligations at each point of the year. That is readily illustrated by the cycle of arable faming in which money is spent from the time when crops are established but income is only received when the crop is sold. That also demonstrates the need for working capital to fund the costs of seeds, fertilisers, sprays, machinery and other costs.

5.4.2   A cash flow forecast working from the start of the accounting period, typically month by month, can both:
- set out the expected pattern of expenditure and income and so its cash flow and net cash position, planning any need for borrowing
- take account through the year of any changes that may require remedial action.

5.5   Management Accounts
5.5.1   These offer a means to record and monitor the performance of the business as the year unfolds, with income and expenditure set against the budget and previous years' figures to enable comparison, challenge and understanding as well as any changes in business policy that may be promoted as the outcome changes, whether for better or worse than previously projected. This supports the management approach of "Measure, Monitor, Manage" with perpetual revision of the business in response – though this can be harder for many farming businesses with the inflexibility of enterprises that have annual cycles.

5.5.2   Management accounts have to be interpreted sensibly as there can always be reasons why both income and expenditure can arise earlier or later than originally expected or for figures to vary in other ways. Nonetheless, they are a tool to aid understanding and critical analysis of both the current operation of the business and its future improvement.

5.6   Farm Management Accounting
5.6.1   Leading analysts like Derek Barber developed the conventional and widely used system of farm management accounting which has gained sway from the 1960s.

5.6.2   Wrestling with the perpetual problem of how overheads should be apportioned, it separates out:
- the variable costs that change with the size of the enterprise in question. For wheat, the variable costs re the costs of seeds, sprays and fertilisers, which will increase proportionately with each extra acre grown and reduce in proportion to a reduction in the acreage
- the fixed costs (or overheads) of such items as labour, machinery, building repairs and finance charges which do not change automatically with any change in the scale of the business.

5.6.3   Its approach is:
- to identify the operational enterprises on the farm, such as wheat, barley or suckler cows
- for each enterprise to determine its gross margin by:
  ○ taking the expected yield from an acre of arable ground or a head of livestock and multiplying it by the expected price to give a sales figure per acre/head
  ○ deducting the variable costs for that enterprise, again as a per acre/head figure
- the gross margins for all the enterprises can then be totalled to give the farm gross margin
- the fixed costs can then be deducted from that farm gross margin to give an overall outcome.

5.6.4   This approach has proved a powerful analytical tool for understanding and improving the economics of commodity production. In particular, it has framed the argument that a major way to reduce the unit cost of production of a commodity is to increase its scale so spreading the fixed costs over more acres, including the use of larger machines to spread the cost of the driver. We may be entering times when that proposition is more open to challenge when considering individual cases.

5.6.5   This can be refined with closer knowledge of actual performance of the farm and what yields and costs can be expected from different areas of the farm, so coming to understanding the varying contributions to the business from each part.

5.6.6   The outcome can then be tested for different assumptions in yields and prices.

5.6.7   This also allows partial budgets (see below). Where a gross margin for an enterprise or area of an enterprise is negative, that part of the business is then not making any contribution to helping pay for the overheads and so costs the business money rather than supporting profit. That might simply be a function of prices thought to be temporarily low and so potentially to be remedied by changes in markets that are foreseen as reasonably likely. However, that apparently practical reasoning should not be an excuse to avoid facing up to real pressures requiring change.

5.6.8   Even a modest gross margin is still helping to pay towards overheads, needing closer judgment as to whether it is actually worth staying with that part of the operation, as abandoning it is likely to leave the farm's fixed costs unchanged.

5.6.9   In some cases, there may be a justification for an enterprise which does not yield a gross margin as it may contribute to the business in other ways than an express financial margin.

5.6.10   It should be possible to see through the weak performance of an enterprise in the adverse circumstances of one year (as with a dip in process or poor yields) rather than accurately reflecting a long term trend. The risk, though, is of failing to recognise underlying shifts in markets or circumstances that may threaten the business. This is an exercise in using a sense of perspective to avoid "knee-jerk" reactions.

5.6.11   It might also be that one crop, unviable in itself, gives enough of an advantage to another crop to warrant devoting resources to it. Thus, a poor cereals crop may still give a good entry for a successful potato crop following it.

5.6.12   One example sometimes seen is the benefit to a larger farm shop from having on-farm production, with varied enterprises that are not viable in their own right. They may meet the volumes required by the shop with its margins and also giving the shop added credibility in the market, even though it may also buy such produce in to maintain the year-round sales and broader range demanded by most customers.

5.6.13   With the structure and detail of the CAAV's Costings of Agricultural Operations, it is possible to allocate machinery costs to variable costs based on actual usage, and then making an appropriate reduction to fixed costs.

5.6.14   Larger and more computerised farm businesses may have their own precise costings for machinery use, allocating it to specific operations, crops and land parcels. Detailed labour records may assist a similar allocation.

5.6.15   Despite the terminology being used, it is useful to note that, for controlling the business:
- variable costs are frequently difficult to change with experience or advice on the optimal seed rates and applications rates for fertilisers and sprays to achieve a proper yield
- fixed costs are often more easy to change, as by achieving greater efficiency in machinery and, where used, labour.

5.7   Servicing Debt

5.7.1   With the external finance for farm businesses usually provided by borrowing from the bank, one important issue is the ability of the business to service existing or proposed debt.

5.7.2   Once a business has met its operating costs, any surplus is there to:
- repay debt
- make new or replacement investment
- reward its owners, both with current income but also longer term provision for retirement

with any remaining surplus after those potentially competing claims then in reserve against more difficult days.

5.7.3   Debt repayment requires both:
- the payment of interest on the loan. It is likely that any debt taken out since 2008 will be at lower rates of interest than for older loans. Money borrowed on overdraft will be dearer than money borrowed on agreed loans while lending secured on land will usually be cheaper still
- the repayment of the amount borrowed. That might be as regular and predictable payments in tranches (as with a domestic mortgage) or as a lump sum at the end but either way that has to be funded. A bank may allow an overdraft to run on indefinitely but it is vulnerable to be reviewed or recalled in a way that an agreed term loan or a mortgage should not be.

5.7.4   When looking at the business overall, does it provide enough income to meet the calls on it, including the current servicing costs of debt? If not, the business is at some risk that should require some action. That analysis may raise a question about the level of drawings by the business owners as well as about the operation of the business itself.

5.7.5   In some cases, it can be possible to reduce interest costs by consolidating existing unsecured loans at a lower rate by securing the borrowed money against land. A lender might be able to offer lower interest rates on the basis of a current value for owned land, strengthening the balance sheet where a historic cost has been used.

5.7.6   While farming is a sector of generally prudent lenders and borrowers, it is the borrower who accepts the responsibility for repayment. Burdening the business and its owners with unsustainable debt may be creating or compounding a problem that is bigger than the one to be solved.

5.7.7   When looking a specific project that requires borrowing to fund it, the question is then whether the project is capable of servicing and repaying that loan as well as of what return it might give on that investment.

5.8 Reviewing Business or Investment Proposals

5.8.1 Introduction – While some expenditure is simply a matter of necessity or for compliance, an investment or a business development proposal will typically involve incurring cost in the hope of improving income, reducing cost or both, perhaps with gains in efficiency or quality. This could be anything form buying more land to enlarging a dairy herd, buying a significant machine, erecting a building or looking at a diversification.

5.8.2 That could require justifying the spending as a use of money already available to the business, when that money might have other uses (considering the opportunity cost as well as the possible return).

5.8.3 Equally, and especially for larger projects, it might require borrowing or reassuring an existing lender. The costs of borrowing will then be an additional cost of the project while the business also assumes the burden of the repaying the money borrowed (the principal).

5.8.4 Accounting techniques are used to model proposed schemes and so assist decision making alongside any other criteria or issues relevant to the business.

5.8.5 It is worth testing major projects for their vulnerability to significant overruns in the time to implement them and their costs – both of which frequently occur. Assumptions on these points can often prove unrealistically optimistic in failing to allow for the practical issues that arise with any major work.

5.8.6 It is also worth taking account of non-financial issues, whether costs or benefits. These can include the potential cost to then business of diverting the management capacity of the business to the project away from its ordinary activity.

5.8.7 Partial Budgeting – A partial budget is just that, a budget for the part of the business that would be changed by the proposal, assuming the rest of the business remains unchanged, so focusing on the financial effect of the suggested change.

5.8.8. A partial budget sets out only the costs and returns that would change with implementing the proposal, so requiring analysis of what might be involved, how things might change, what the costs might be and what the returns might be and so the overall change for the business foreseen from this proposal and whether it is financially viable.

5.8.9 It should be checked that the partial budget does capture all the effects of the proposal on the business.

5.8.10 It will not typically take account of the effects, if any, of the suggested change on capital values or tax treatment, which if real, would need to be considered subsequently as part of the decision making process.

5.8.11 A partial budget can be used to judge competing options such as replacing a grain store or buying capacity in a grain pool. The results from preparing a partial budget for each option can then be compared and considered alongside all the other factors. That example might prompt consideration of whether the available grain pool has a better record on selling grain well than the farmer.

5.8.12 In considering a proposed change in farm operations, there may be:
- cost savings in labour, repairs, disease losses or other points
- costs incurred in the project, its finance, income displaced by changing land use
- improved income from greater production or production that can be marketed better.

5.8.13 A classic example is where a dairy farmer considers contracting out the rearing of heifers with:
- possible savings in the costs of labour, feed, bedding, veterinary matters
- possibly greater income from using the capacity released to milk more cows but also the costs associated with that
- the charges made by the person taking on rearing of the heifers
- possible new uses for land and buildings used by the heifers with any costs or income associated with that
- any finance involved in adapting buildings from heifer rearing to other purposes.

That assessment can then be put alongside other reasons that might have prompted considering withdrawing from heifer rearing.

5.8.14 Reviewing the figures in the partial budget for possible cost overruns or savings, delays in securing new income or the risks of lower output prices, increased finance costs or other risks can be used to test the robustness of the proposal – a sensitivity analysis.

5.8.15 Return on Investment (RoI) – This is a way of testing the prospective return on an investment or project over a given period of time, with a percentage using the formula

$$\frac{\text{Profit added over the given period by the project}}{\text{Cost of investment}} \times 100$$

5.8.16 That assumes that all the investment is at the start of the project and would become more complex if it is to take account of expected subsequent investment in the project.

5.8.17 If the partial budget shows that the project:
- would cost the business £100,000
- is estimated to offer the business £15,000 a year in net profit

then over one year the RoI would be 15%. That figure would reach 100% in the seventh year (the **payback period**). It is for the business to judge if that is acceptable or not.

5.8.18 As for other tools, the results of varying the costs and income figures can be used to test the robustness of the proposal.

5.8.19 Internal Rate of Return (IRR) – This a more sophisticated measure of the potential profitability and so the potential return on a capital investment and is more commonly used for larger businesses or specific projects such as wind turbines. While RoI reports the total growth over the specified period, IRR is the annual rate of growth.

5.8.20 The IRR is the discount rate that makes the net present value (NPV) of all the cash flows from a project equal to zero, that is the rate that would be needed to make the current value of the future benefits equal to the initial investment costs. It is "internal" in that it is based on the cash flows from the project and not on external factors such as the cost of capital (which may still be relevant to the final decision).

5.8.21   It thus uses the same formula as that for NPV, requiring the NPV to be zero with a facility offered by Excel for this, though to be used cautiously.

5.8.22   The higher the IRR, the more likely it is that the project is worth undertaking, provided that it is above the cost of capital required and above any rate of return required by the business.

5.8.23   It can be used to compare differing or alternative projects on a broadly similar basis so that, depending on their relative costs of finance and any non-financial criteria, the project with the highest IRR would be favoured. That is a measure of rate of growth expected from the project.

5.8.24   One example of such a comparison is between investing in upgrading an existing facility and replacing it with a new one.

5.8.205 A more developed variant, modifying the rate of return by applying a risk free rate to the incremental returns, tackles the problems that:
  – it may be hard to reinvest the cash flows at the same rate and so a simple IRR calculation can overstate the potential future value
  – are caused by swings between positive and negative future cash flows moderating the result.

5.8.26   Other cautions about using IRR include:
  – the difficulty of comparing projects with different lives. Ac short term project may have a high IRR but a low NPV. A longer term project with a lower IRR may add more value to the business
  – more generally, a project with a low IRR but a high NPV may add much value but do so slowly.

6. ANALYSIS OF ACCOUNTS
"Making the Accounts Talk"

6.1 Introduction

6.1.1 The accounts may be seen as an obligation but they should not be regarded as impenetrable and of no further use, but rather as a means of extracting and offering valuable information about the business. This chapter looks at approaches and tools to help achieve that and aid analysis of each of the profit and loss account, the balance sheet and, where provided, the flow of funds statement with the interconnections between them with issues, trends, risks and opportunities that may show.

6.1.2 Initial key questions include:
- what does the business do?
- what are its sources of income?
- what do they depend on?
- what are the associated costs?
- what drives those costs?
- how have these changed?

6.1.3 Any one set of accounts can only be a snapshot. Thus, having several – say, three – years of accounts can make it easier to see trends and issues and see beyond the individual circumstances of any single year. Historic analysis provides a basis for:
- assessing past performance
- testing the robustness of future projections

so, with future forecasts, giving a fuller, if somewhat speculative, analysis of the direction of the business and its prospects for the future.

6.1.4 How far back any analysis of accounts should go will turn on the nature of the business and the accessibility of the information. However, it is very difficult to make any meaningful assessment with less than three years' data; if available and relevant, five may offer a more robust picture. There may be occasions where it is helpful to look back further, as where there have been strategic changes in direction of the business which might now be reversed or in very volatile sectors. However, the more historic the data are, the greater will be the need for care, understanding and adjustment.

6.2 Measures of Income in Farm Accounting

6.2.1 The structures developed for farm accounting noted above result in standard approaches to find the outturn for the business, including Net Farm Income (NFI), Management and Investment Income (MII) and now Farm Business Income (FBI). As widely recognised and standard measures, they assist benchmarking the business against other similar farms.

6.2.2 Net Farm Income (NFI) – This was developed on a standardised basis to give a consistent measure of the profitability of the farming activity itself, by using the assumptions that all businesses are tenancies and have no debt. That allows farms with different business structures, tenures and indebtedness to be compared on a like-for-like basis.

6.2.3 That means it is assessed:
- with an imputed rent for owner-occupied land and buildings and for landlord-type improvements
- with no deductions made for interest payments on any farming loans, overdrafts or mortgages and also excluding any interest earned on financial assets.

Thus, it represents the return to the farmer and spouse alone for their manual and managerial labour and on the tenant-type capital invested in the farm business.

6.2.4   As other partners and directors are then not taken into account, a deduction is also made for any unpaid labour provided by non-principal partners and directors, their spouses and by others; valued at average local market rates for manual agricultural work.

6.2.5   Management and Investment Income (MII) – This measure was long used by the universities in reporting to the Farm Business Survey. It is defined as the return to the farmer and spouse for their management and on the tenant-type capital of the business, not on their own labour.

6.2.6   Management and investment income is found by subtracting an imputed cost for the manual labour of the farmer and spouse form Net Farm Income.

6.2.7   Such measures based on a purely agricultural assessment may be less appropriate where the business has substantial non-agricultural activity though they could still be used for the agricultural part of such a business. That and other concerns has led the use now in official reporting of Farm Business Income (FBI).

6.2.8   Farm Business Income – FBI income from diversified activities, being non-agricultural activities using farm resources.

6.2.9   For sole traders and partnerships, Farm Business Income measures the financial return:
- to all unpaid labour (farmers and their spouses, non-principal partners and their spouses and family workers) and
- on all their capital invested in the farm business, including land and buildings.

6.2.10   For businesses operating as companies, Farm Business Income is the financial return on the shareholder's capital invested in the farm business, with directors' remuneration now being deducted.

6.2.11   FBI is seen as essentially the same as Net Profit and so comparable with measures for other businesses, in and outside agriculture. However, there are differences as FBI, based on farm management accounting will, for example, treat:
- treat stocks at market value while Net Profit, based on general accounting principles, will use the cost of production
- assess depreciation on current replacement value rather than Net Profit's use of historic cost.

6.2.12   With difference noted between the assessment of FBI for companies and for other business structures, that has been further standardised as Farm Corporate Income and Farm Investment Income.

6.2.13   Farm Corporate Income – This reports the return to the business on its own capital invested in the farm business, to risk and to entrepreneurship.

6.2.14   It is found by deducting unpaid labour, both manual and managerial, from Farm Business Income and so allows the profitability of sole traders and partnerships to be compared directly with that of companies. However, while there are recognised techniques for placing value on unpaid manual labour, the value of unpaid managerial labour is harder to ascertain.

6.2.15   Farm Investment Income – This reports on the return on all capital invested in the farm business (whether it is borrowed or not), to risk and to entrepreneurship.

6.2.16   It is found by adding net interest payments to Farm Corporate Income and so has the same uncertainty as Farm Corporate Income.

6.2.17   Other measures that may be found include:
- **Occupier's Net Income (ONI)** – This is the return to the farmer and spouse for their manual and managerial labour and on all their assets invested in the farm business, including land and buildings. It does not make the assumption that land is tenanted. It does not include the labour of the farmer and spouse labour but interest payments on farming loans (net of any receipts) of interest are deducted.
- **Cash Income** – This is the difference between total revenue (receipts adjusted for debtors) and total expenditure (purchases adjusted for creditors) so assuming that all end of year debtor and creditor payments are settled in full. It is thus the cash return to all the owners of the business for their manual and managerial labour and on all their investment in the business.
- **Family Farm Income** – This is a measure of farm income used by the European Commission. Based upon actual tenure and indebtedness, it is a broader measure than Net Farm Income as it represents the return to all unpaid labour (not just the farmer and spouse). It also includes breeding livestock stock appreciation even though that cannot be realised without reducing the productive capacity of the farm.

6.3   EBITDA

6.3.1   A measure commonly used for assessing the underlying capacity of a business to generate net income is EBITDA, that is Earnings Before Interest, Tax, Depreciation and Amortisation.

6.3.2   Excluding those items enables a view of a business before considering:
- how it is financed, whether by equity or debt, loans at different rates or terms
- how it is taxed, as say between a company and partnership
- accounting issues, such as over the timing of past capital investment.

so that the assessment is of the actual operation of the business.

6.3.3   This also assists with the comparison of the operating performance of different businesses, even where they have differences in financing or are subject to different tax treatment or bands.

6.4   Sensitivity Analysis

6.4.1   Any single set of accounts can only offer snapshot as at a date within the circumstances relevant to it. Yet planning a business has to take the possible changes in those circumstances into account. Testing accounts, budgets and projections for such changes as varying yields, prices, interest rates, or cost factors is usually called sensitivity analysis. This is an essential tool, showing how changes in output, prices or costs would affect the business.

6.4.2   Undertaking sensitivity analysis can show how vulnerable or not a business might be to possible changes and so help judge the risks it faces or that should be taken into account in reviewing any proposal.

6.5   Accounting Ratios

6.5.1   Among the tools used to look at accounts are a variety of ratios, known as accounting ratios or financial ratios, between different figures in the accounts that can help understand strengths and weaknesses in the business. Easily set up in Excel, they should be seen as a starting point for questions in finding out what is really happening and allow comparison with other similar businesses.

6.5.2   They look at such matters as:
– solvency – does the business have value?
– liquidity – can the business meet its obligations quickly
– profitability
– efficiency.

Designed for wide range of businesses, some will not be as apt for farming and rural businesses as others but could be more relevant where the business has a retail or processing element.

6.5.3   As farming businesses frequently have land in their accounts at historic cost, the effective use of ratios using asset and capital values will require a view as to the current value of the land, rather than what is shown in the balance sheet.

6.5.4   Such ratios include:
– the various profitability ratios, including
  ○ gross margin – the turnover of an enterprise before overheads. In farming this is often done for each internal enterprise, such as wheat (typically expressed at a cash sum of £/acre), but can also be done for the overall business and is typically expressed as percentage of turnover:

$$\frac{\text{Sales} - \text{Cost of Goods Sold}}{\text{Sales}}$$

  ○ return on assets:

$$\frac{\text{Net Income}}{\text{Total assets}}$$

  ○ return on equity (the capital that the business owner has in the business)
  ○ return on capital employed:

$$\frac{\text{Net Profit}}{\text{Capital employed}}$$

– the various solvency ratios, including
  ○ the debt to equity ratio (also known as gearing) – for a sole trader or partnership this is:

$$\frac{\text{Loans and bank overdrafts}}{\text{Capital}}$$

  ○ the debt to assets ratio
  ○ the ratio of debt to earnings
  ○ the interest coverage ratio
– the various liquidity ratios, including
  ○ the net current assets ratio

$$\frac{\text{Current assets}}{\text{Current liabilities}}$$

A ratio of 2 will show that the business has twice as much in current assets as it has in current liabilities

- the liquid capital ratio (also the quick ratio), measuring the business' ability to meet its short term obligations by using its most liquid assets. This excludes stocks. It is found by the calculation:

$$\frac{\text{Current assets minus stocks}}{\text{Current liabilities}}$$

A ratio of 1 is commonly thought strong for many businesses.

- the working capital ratio
- the defensive interval, testing how long a business could survive without cash coming in:

$$\frac{\text{Liquid assets}}{\text{Daily operating expenses}}$$

- payout ratio – the share of profit paid out to the owners of the business
- the typical efficiency ratios may be more appropriate for businesses with a faster turnover of stocks than farming but include:
  - stocks turnover ratio

$$\frac{((\text{Opening stocks + closing stocks})/2) \times 365}{\text{Cost of sales}}$$

  - days sales in stocks
- the various coverage ratios, including:
  - times interest earned
  - debt service coverage ratio
- perhaps more relevant to businesses undertaking multiple sales and offering credit, including some horticultural business, diversified businesses and members' own businesses (particularly livestock markets) are ratios relevant to liquidity such as
  - debtor days – what is the average number of days for customers to pay a bill from the business.

7. BENCHMARKING AND OTHER INFORMATION
"Measure, Manage, Monitor"

7.1   The Use of Performance Indicators
"More than half of farmers operating in the bottom quartile do not realise they are underachieving, ..." The Characteristics of High Performing Farms in the UK, AHDB and Andersons (October 2018), para 2.2

7.1.1   Accounts and their analysis are a powerful tool for assessing the performance of a business, both in absolute terms and relative to others. The analysis of accounts can produce measures that enable one business to be compared with other similar businesses, potentially offering illumination in understand where strengths and weaknesses lie in a farm or other business.

7.1.2   Especially with the present concern over agricultural productivity, other measures of a business' performance are important to managing it, alongside the financial data and insights from accounts. These include measures of physical and technical performance in which the same wide differences are seen between the top and bottom quartiles in any sector.

7.1.3   Whether for financial or physical performance, the use of wider market information for assessment and comparison, using knowledge of the position of the business against the average and knowing how the top performers (often top quartile) are doing can greatly aid the process of business improvement. It can challenge complacency, show where attention might be best devoted and open questions that might not otherwise have been asked.

7.1.4   Thus, long ago prompted by National Milk Records and other services, a dairy enterprise might monitor indicators including basic facts about production and then measures of inputs and margins, such as:
- average yield per cow
- average milk price
- butterfat percentage
- protein percentage
- tonnes of concentrates per cow
- kilogrammes of concentrates per litre of milk
- cost of purchased feed per litre
- herd margin over concentrates
- margins over concentrates per cow
- margin over concentrates per litre

as well as health measures, especially with the increasing use of modern technology to monitor cows, from movement to nutrition.

7.1.5   Already closely watched in their detail by many dairy, pig and poultry farmers, the volume of data that will come from modern technology will put more focus on this with businesses identifying and then watching and using key performance indicators (KPIs).

7.1.6   Once appropriate measures are identified and measured, they can be reviewed and assessed, aiding management and control of the business and informing decisions about change. They can also be compared not only with the figures in management handbooks and costings guides but also, where possible, with other similar businesses, whether through discussion groups or by reference to collective but anonymised, and so potentially more objective, data.

7.2 Benchmarking

7.2.1   This process of crystallising data on a standard basis and comparing it with others has come to be called benchmarking.

7.2.2   Facilities for this may be offered by voluntary discussion groups or through farm consultants as well as, perhaps more officially, by organisations such as the Agricultural and Horticultural Development Board (AHDB) or colleges such as CAFRE in Northern Ireland.

7.2.3   In particular, the AHDB offers its free *Farmbench* service to help farmers evaluate the performance of their beef, lamb, dairy, combinable crop, potato and sugar beet enterprises, by comparing agreed performance indicators with neighbouring, local or national farmers. As well as enabling internal review by the business, the results and best practice can be discussed other farmers through Business Improvement Groups as part of the process of working from the evidence to decisions about improving individual profitability and productivity.

7.2.4   The Welsh Farming Connect offers its *Measure to Manage* benchmarking service for farming and forestry, supported by advice and mentoring.

7.2.5   Some buyers of produce promote benchmarking such as the Sainsbury's Dairy Development Group which records and shares data form its dairy farming suppliers, covering key indicators for animal health and welfare as part of production measures. Sainsburys sees this as assisting its dairy farmers to achieve a 45 per cent reduction in clinical mastitis and a 47 per cent reduction in lameness.

7.3 Accounting Benchmarks

7.3.1   These indicators are among those commonly used for reviewing farm businesses.

7.3.2   *Full Economic Margin* – This, similar to Net Farm Income, is the margin left to pay tax, repay borrowings and reinvest. Pension contributions or other retirement provision might also be a call on this. A positive value is essential here for the business not to lose ground.

7.3.3   It is assessed by:
- taking income from production (including valuation changes)
- deducting all payments for production costs with depreciation, the value of all unpaid labour and rental value of owned land.

In looking ahead at the post-BPS world, direct payments and other subsidies should be excluded.

7.3.4   *Full Economic Cost of Production* – This is an assessment of the costs of production, a critical area of control for commodity production businesses.

7.3.5   It is assessed by taking the total of purchases for production, including depreciation. It can again also include the value of unpaid labour and the rental value of owned land; knowing whether this has been done will assist comparison.

7.3.6   For comparative purposes, it can then be divided by area or another standard measure such as per tonne or per litre of production.

7.3.7   *Whole Farm Return on Tenant's Capital* – This assesses the return on the capital that a tenant would ordinarily employ and so excludes land and buildings, and is thus based on the capital in the farming operation. It offers an indication of the business' ability to generate a return and brings the balance sheet (typically strong) together with the profit and loss account (typically less so).

7.3.8   Expressed as a percentage, the approaches to this take the income less the full economic cost of production and then divide the result by the tenant's capital. Variations include or exclude unpaid labour.

7.3.9   *Fixed Costs Ratio* – With fixed costs often more controllable than variable costs, this expresses the total of labour, power, machinery and other overheads as a percentage of income.

7.3.10   Understanding that percentage for each component can identify particular issues for attention.

7.4   Physical Benchmarks

7.4.1   As examples, the AHDB has offered these examples as to more relevant specific figures for different enterprises:

Cereals/Oilseeds
- seed costs (£/t)
- inorganic fertiliser costs (£/t)
- crop protection cost (£/t)

Potatoes
- nematicides (£/t)
- storage costs (£/t)
- diesel usage (l/ha)

Block Calving Dairy
- milk solids output (kg/ha)
- milk yield from forage
- cows and heifers calved in the first six weeks (%)

All Year Round Calving Dairy Herds
- pregnancy rate (%)
- age at first calving (months)
- dairy purchased feed costs (ppl)

Beef Sucklers
- 200 day weaned calf weight as percentage of cow weight
- age at first calving (months)
- cows and heifers calved in the first six weeks (%)

Beef Finishing
- daily liveweight gain (kg/day)
- cattle hitting target specification for regular outlet (%)

Breeding Flock
- lambs reared per 100 ewes put to the tup (%)
- lamb losses from scanning to rearing (%)
- average weight at weaning (kg)

Lamb Finishing
- daily liveweight gain (kg)
- lambs hitting target specification (%)

Breeding/Weaning Pigs
- pigs weaned per sow and per litter
- average weaned piglet weight
- vet and med costs including in-feed medication per sow.

Pig Finishing
- mortality in the last month or last batch (%)
- vet cost per pig over the last 12 months (£/head)
- daily liveweight gain (last six months or last batch) (kg/day)

7.4.2   In addition to the work of the AHDB, there is a growing number of other benchmarking initiatives from farmer discussion groups to industry data such as the *Results of the Red Meat Benchmarking Project* published in June 2019 by Hybu Cig Cymru (Meat Promotion Wales) reviewing Welsh sheep and suckler cow enterprises.

7.4.3   When judging tractors and other power units on a farm, comparison can be made on a horsepower per unit of area basis.

7.5   Reviewing Markets
7.5.1   While benchmarking may most often be thought of for farming as about the costs and production performance that is of particular importance to running a commodity business, it is also important to review sales performance and beyond that markets more generally.

7.5.2   Skills in farming do not necessarily include the skills needed for selling produce. Livestock famers take advantage of auctions to sell animals and there can be advantages in having grain sold through marketing organisations where they offer the advantages of volume, flexibility including blending, skill and market knowledge. This might also be a lesser cost than may be needed to replace or enlarge grain storage on the farm

7.5.3   When looking ahead, it could be material to watch market trends as to what does and might sell well and what does not. This may be particularly critical where exposed to changing market trends and the opportunities of new export markets.

7.6   Other Information
7.6.1   Another recent but very important development in the information that can be available to a farm business comes from the mapping now possible through new technology, supporting and illuminating the information that has been available in the past from experience, surface surveys and nutrient analyses.

7.6.2   In particular, GPS mapping and the technology on modern machinery allows such work as:
- yield mapping
- soil structure surveys, showing better and worse areas with and pattern of compaction
- gross margin mapping

which in turn can then feed into larger decisions about land management, cropping, land use and allocation of areas to environmental work as well over the varying the applications of fertilisers for different parts of fields and so improving efficiency and cost control and margin.

7.6.3   They also support such techniques as controlled traffic farming and, potentially, driverless machinery.

7.6.4   While now more widely done for arable operations, these have the same value to offer to pasture-based businesses.

7.7   Review and Act on the Knowledge

"Critically, taking that information to the farm to identify what you can do to farm more profitably is what matters. Knowledge is only useful if you change something as a response." (The Characteristics of High Performing Farms in the UK, AHDB and Andersons (October 2018), page 66)

7.7.1   None of this offers anything more than a possible description of business, if it not used positively in management to prompt discussion and change. The information gathered from benchmarking, accounts and other tools is a starting point for action, perhaps first by understanding the issues indicated by the figures and then moving to do something about them.

7.7.2   Once decisions are taken, they need to be implemented and then their effects reviewed in a continuous cycle of improvement.

7.7.3   While some businesses may need more fundamental change, others will simply need a culture of steady improvement in all aspects, with small gains at each point multiplying to give a larger overall improvement.

7.7.4   Discussion groups, perhaps based on benchmarking, can be one way of sustaining this effort with mutual comparison and review as well as technical exchanges and the stimulus or seeing and working with others going through the same process. Thee may often be a role for an adviser in bringing such group together and supporting it in going forward.

8. FINANCE

8.1 Where Might Money Come From?

8.1.1 Where might the money for operating and developing the business come from?

8.1.2 Businesses need:
- working capital, particularly important for farming with the annual or longer cycle of production for many enterprises between first cost and the sale of produce
- capital for investment, whether normal routine work or for more substantial matters like new buildings or land purchase.

They may on occasion need to meet substantial calls for money out of the business, as where someone leaves a partnership, a non-farming family member wants to realise value in their land ownership, social care has to be funded, a regulatory need requires major spending, there is a divorce or a large tax liability arises.

8.1.3 The financial strength of a business lies not only in the capital it owns but also in the extent to which it can reasonably borrowing with an assessment of its available collateral to support borrowing and its creditworthiness. Owned farmland has long been a valuable form of collateral for loans, with loans that are secured on it typically having lower interest rates than for many other forms of borrowing. Banks do not accept a tenancy or the expectation of end of tenancy compensation as potential security offering an equivalent collateral value though the more secure the tenancy the more it will assist the business in its relationship with a lender. An overdraft or loan may require a charge, fixed or floating, in favour of the lender over the farm's assets such as livestock and machinery.

8.1.4 While there is much discussion of farm borrowing, not only is it overall relatively low when compared to the value of agricultural assets but banks report that a substantial fraction of farmers do not borrow but have deposits with them.

8.1.5 Whatever the need, the money required should be seen as having a cost.

8.1.6 Where the money is already apparently available in the business, spending it on one purpose prevents it from being used for other purposes in which it might earn a better return – the **opportunity cost** – requiring assumptions about the other possible uses of the money or the business' borrowing capacity, its potential yield and risk.

8.1.7 There may also be the question of whether spending that money compromises the liquidity of the business, by reducing the ready funds that makes it able to meet its bills as they arise.

8.1.8 Money may come from other family members who may then nonetheless want some claim on or involvement in the business, perhaps as a mortgagee or as a partner, if only to protect the value of their commitment whether or not they seek a return on it.

8.1.9 Equity Investment? – While private equity investment in business is a feature of the wider economy with capital put into the business by third parties who take a share of the ownership and its returns, farming and estate operations do not naturally look beyond family members for outside investment.

8.1.10 Culturally alien, that is also because:
- many such businesses are small scale making the transactions costs of committing equity and active investor involvement daunting

- a reluctance to allow non-family members to have any claim on owned land
- a resistance to third parties being involved in the business
- the typically low rates of return on most agricultural investments.

8.1.11   While there is a little more use of crowd funding (see below) to raise capital for some projects, EU State Aid rules mean that farming and market gardening along with renewable energy and some other sectors are excluded from the Enterprise Investment Scheme (EIS) and the Seed Enterprise Investment Scheme (SEIS) with their tax advantages for investors in relatively new companies.

8.1.12   Borrowing – Thus, farms and estates requiring money from outside the business typically borrow and lenders have found this a good area in which to lend, provided that they are comfortable with the borrower's ability to meet the costs of the loan and repay it.

8.2   Conventional Lending

8.2.1   Operationally, many farms rely on **merchant credit**, the delay in paying for goods from merchants which can, with tolerance, be linked to the production cycle or the timing of harvest, at the least easing cash flow in the short term but still a liability on the business. Such merchant credit may be linked to commitments to sell produce through the merchant.

8.2.2   Banks are then the prime source of lending finance for rural operations, typically in one of three general forms:
- **overdraft** finance – short term borrowing within an agreed limit that, in effect, extends the current account enabling payments to be made and honoured within the set limit. Overdrafts can help with farming's working capital cycle, easing the troughs in short term cash flow. The overdraft limit can be reviewed, potentially being reduced or even withdrawn, and will come with the costs of a fee and an interest charge on its use. Charges on spending beyond that limit, where allowed, can be expensive. There will not normally be a penalty for clearing the overdraft.
- specific **loans** with an agreed sum being lent for a stated period (usually several years) with an agreed schedule for payments and repayment. This medium term borrowing can suit the funding of an investment project with the finance costs known in advance and fixed. There may be a cost to early repayment.
- **mortgages**, where the loan is secured on land that is pledged as security for the money borrowed. The borrower is the mortgagor and the lender the mortgagee. These are often longer term loans, commonly over decades, and can have lower interest costs because of the quality of the security for the repayment. However, assets used as security for a loan can be repossessed by the lender. The terms of mortgage may limit the borrower's ability to use the property in certain ways, such as letting it or seeking a further mortgage on it, to protect the value of its security.

8.2.3   Securing this finance is likely to require providing the increasing amounts of financial and other information that banks, themselves subject to greater regulation, require. Banks are increasingly focussed on the ability of the business to service the loan (see 5.7.1 above), not only on the security offered by the land. With the new regulation of lenders, the ability to service the proposed loan may be tested to show it could withstand significantly higher interest rates. They may also look for evidence that the applicant is a reliable and competent business owner with integrity and so could seek evidence of active financial management and use of such techniques as benchmarking.

8.2.4 The lender of an overdraft or a loan may seek to take a charge over the working assets of the farm, such its livestock and machinery. This may be a fixed charge linked to certain assets or floating charge covering any assets up to the value of the debt. That can give the lender some assurance as to its loan but, where an overdraft can be recalled, is a risk for the business.

8.2.5 With concerns in the 1920s about the ability of farming, then largely tenanted, to invest, the Agricultural Credit Acts 1928 and 1932 enable a tenant to pledge farming stock and tenant right against loans. Use of such facilities largely lapsed with the use of fixed and floating changes though there was some exploration of this when milk quota had substantial value with rights to compensation on the end of the tenancy compensation. In practice, the combination of relatively low and uncertain values and the difficulty for the lender in realising them militates against this source of finance.

8.2.6 The costs of loans are related to the cost to the banks of raising money at the time when the terms are agreed. Some of that is driven by interest rates in the economy and money needed by the bank to attract deposits to enable lending. The regulation of banks under the Basel agreements and, in the EU the Capital Requirements Regulation implementing them, requires them to hold reserves to protect their financial stability – higher reserves are required for less secure loans so making them more expensive.

8.2.7 Where money has been borrowed at fixed rates or over a fixed term, it is likely that there will be some penalties for early repayment, as the bank will have made arrangements for funding such loans with its own costs in doing so.

8.2.8 Unlike residential mortgages, mortgages on agricultural land are typically for loans of not more than 50 or 60 per cent of the value of the land, partly reflecting the limits on repayment placed by conventional farm incomes but making them secure with very low records of repossession, let alone loss to the lender.

8.2.9 Other Financial Structures – Looking beyond agricultural lending, other financial structures are used for development projects, typically with the money being released by the lender in phases as each stage of the project is completed and the underlying asset gains in value with the increasing prospect of completion and so greater certainty about the remaining risks involved.

More expensive and technological projects, such as larger wind turbines or controlled environment farming developments, may be handled as **project finance** by banks or venture capital and private equity houses. This will see a higher level of due diligence and appraisal of the risk involved but can give access to higher sums, whether as loans or equity, probably using a **special purpose vehicle (SPV)** for the project. Usually a company, this is a business entity solely devoted to the project and containing its risks, enabling it to be transferred to other investors.

8.2.10 Most farms that borrow do so from the main high street lenders who often still have teams of staff dedicated to agricultural work and with a knowledge of the sector. Some, perhaps more often estates, bank with and borrow from more specialist houses specialising in high net worth individuals. Some of these have offered particular facilities in managing issues with direct CAP payments, confident in the ultimate payments from the state, a sovereign debtor.

8.2.11 Banks and others are looking at "green finance", seeking opportunities to lend on environmental and social projects; as, for example, Lloyds Bank's Clean Growth Finance Initiative.

8.2.12 Some borrowing, perhaps by those already in some trouble, is also taken from secondary lenders with an appetite for greater risk, often at greater expense or more difficult terms and so a larger prospect of foreclosure on the borrower.

8.2.13 Insurers can also be a source of funds in various ways, largely about the management of risk. Assurance policies can assist with taxation liabilities on death while equity release from property is becoming more common means in the wider economy to raise money, often for retirement or social care but potentially for investment. Life insurance or term assurance can also be a means of recognising a risk in an agreement that might otherwise be difficult to handle between the parties or within the business.

8.3   Innovative Funding/Investing
8.3.1   Recent years have seen the development of other sources of finance such as peer to peer lending and crowd funding.

8.3.2   For the business taking such funding, these can offer relatively low cost funding for propositions which can be good but for which bank lending might not be available within the increasing regulatory restrictions on banks.

8.3.3   Investors are likely to be seeking higher returns than are available in conventional lending markets but may also be looking for projects with which they feel an affinity.

8.3.4   With no single funder necessarily committing a large sum to any one proposal, this can offer a means for funders to spread their risks over a range of projects and a diversity of types of project. Returns are not guaranteed. Investments are not protected and so can be lost. Potentially long term, it might not easy to withdraw money from some projects as there is no established mechanism or market for transferring investments.

8.3.5   However, the growth of crowdfunding has seen more intervention by the Financial Conduct Authority (FCA) with rules since 2014 expecting fair commerce and requiring platforms to be clear about the potential investment risks. They are required to separate the operation of the platform from the funding that has been raised.

8.3.6   In principle, investors are not to invest more than 10 per cent of their net investible assets, that is, their money available having excluded their primary residence, pension and life insurance.

8.3.7   Investment through crowd funded bonds or peer-to-peer loans can be held in an Innovative Finance ISA (IFISA) allowing interest to be received free to tax.

8.3.8   Tax Relief for Investment – Legislation offers a suite of tax relief schemes for private investment in qualifying small new businesses operating as companies:
- the Enterprise Investment Scheme (EIS)
- the Seed Enterprise Investment Scheme (SEIS)
- the Social Investment Tax Relief (SITR) for community companies and charities (including trusts)
- Venture Capital Trusts (VCTs), funds channelling investments.

While EIS and SEIS are generally available for crowd funded investments where the company qualifies, EU State Aid rules exclude farming and market gardening from such schemes, along with renewal energy projects. Other excluded sectors include dealing in land and property development.

8.3.9   However, EIS and SEIS may, subject to their rules, be available for investment in:
   – businesses developing alternative crops or techniques such as hydroponics or controlled environment farming
   – companies offering contracting services to farmers but not doing any in-hand farming
   – non-agricultural diversification operations.

8.4   Crowd Funding

8.4.1   Crowd funding is the recent development of an old model for financing specific projects, now using the internet with a mediating organisation (a platform such as CrowdCube (which has raised some £700 million) or Crowdfunder), to raise money from a larger number of often dispersed and unconnected people to be invested as shares or lent as a bond to a project (and sometimes for the development of project to the point where it can be taken to more ordinary sources of finance).

8.4.2   The project will, for this purpose, typically have to be structured as a company, not as an LLP, partnership or sole trader, and not usually be a subordinate company in a group.

8.4.3   In principle, the model is similar to that for using the internet to secure both donations (as with Just Giving) and the crowd funding of litigation, neither necessarily having commercial motives but structured as a means of investment.

8.4.4   If considering seeking crowdfunding, the business will need a realistic target, a sensible valuation of what is needed, an effective marketing pitch and well-executed communications plan to stimulate as much interest as possible and so:
   – the project should be specific and identifiable rather than be the general funding of an existing business; the former is much more likely to attract an investor
   – it will help to be able to tell a story about it, to attract attention and engage interest for what can be personal decisions by investors
   – the intended outcome should be clear, supported by a budget with accompanying reasoning, preferably reviewed by a third party. This will drive the funding target and be the starting point for any due diligence by potential investors
   – the assessment of costs should include the commission that will be taken by the crowd funding platform, potentially a success fee and a completion fee (partly covering the costs of taking money on-line by credit/debit card).
Typically, the scheme will depend on the stated funding target being met – an all or nothing basis; such an approach is reported as more likely to be successful.

8.4.5   While crowdfunding investment would normally see investors take equity or debt in a business, an alternative, rewards-based, model treats the money raised as pre-payments for the final output. Thus, a vineyard might get initial funding with a corresponding commitment to supply a given volume of wine later; or a dairy farm to future milk supplies. The business retains its equity but at some cost to future income, albeit that the benefit to investors is the saving in the retail cost they might otherwise have incurred while the business might only forgo the wholesale value of its output.

8.4.6   When looking at commercial projects, funders may be attracted by the return offered on a project such as for a renewable energy proposal but also to support those with accompanying social or environmental goals, often for development, innovation and improvement. These are going to need project valuations, and so, where rural, potentially instructions for agricultural valuers.

8.4.7   While more commonly funding rural processing and manufacturing businesses, there are examples of using crowd funding to help start businesses, such as an individual starting a tenancy, investing in equipment and livestock.

8.4.8   The approach is variously used to attract outside money into a wide variety of uses, with those seen for property including:
- buy-to-let investment (such as through the House Crowd or Property Partner)
- building affordable housing or selling environmentally friendly custom-built homes, assisting self-build housing without bank borrowing (such as Hab Housing through CrowdCube)
- some commercial investment
- social experiments such as funding a biodynamic far to preserve it from being sold, leasing it back to its current owners.

8.4.9   Triodos Bank, with a strong focus on the third sector has raised money through crowd funding for such projects as:
- a community bond offering 4.5 per cent for developing fibre optic broadband in the rural north
- a variety of community energy finance proposals including 5 per cent inflation linked bond for hydro energy schemes in the Peak District and Dartmoor

8.4.10   Some crowd funding platforms can secure match funding, usually where the type of project qualifies for match funding under the Rural Development Programme. One example has been the Ayrshire LEADER project working through Crowdfunder to offer up to £5,000 of matching money. Crowdfunder has offered other such projects.

8.5   Peer to Peer (P2P) Lending

8.5.1   Peer-to-peer lending can be seen as the debt/loan version of crowd funding but it is commonly identified as a separate structure, matching lenders with borrowers through an on-line platform that allows much reduced costs in doing this.

8.5.2   Unknown in this form before this century, this form of alternative finance has been growing rapidly, channelling £6 billion in the UK in 2018 with one lender, Funding Circle, now listed on the Stock Exchange. One peer to peer lender active in agricultural matters is Folk2Folk. In 2012 the government, concerned about perceived banking reluctance to lend to smaller companies, lent £20 million by this means and further £40 million in 2014.

8.5.3   Often catering for borrowers with good propositions who cannot meet the requirements of banks with their regulatory restrictions, the platform will charge interest on the loan, deduct a proportion for its operations and then pay the lender the remainder, still at an advantage over the rates paid on deposits by banks. Some platforms allow lenders to choose the borrowers of their money.

8.5.4   Some funds offer their investors protection but, by contrast to bank deposits, there is no statutory guarantee for funds that are lent though the Financial Conduct Authority (FCA) rules require platforms to have arrangements in place for loan agreements to continue if the platform fails. With some well publicised recent failures, the FCA is now further developing its monitoring and regulation of this sector. Lenders are likely to be members of the Peer 2 Peer Finance Association.

8.5.5   The loans can be secured on assets or unsecured. Some platforms allow or enable loans to be sold on as securities, often at a marked discount.

8.5.6   The tasks of the peer to peer platform (or intermediary) typically include:
   – offering an on-line platform to enable borrowers to attract lenders and investors to identify and purchase loans that meet their investment criteria, with marketing to find more lenders and borrowers
   – developing of credit models for loan approvals and pricing, so managing potential default rates
   – verifying the borrower's identity, bank account, employment and income
   – undertaking credit checks on borrowers
   – processing payments from borrowers and forwarding those payments to the lenders who invested in the loan
   – tackling borrowers those who are behind or in default
   – legal compliance and reporting.

9. THE GROWING NEED TO SEE BUSINESS VALUE

9.1   Agricultural valuation has had to undertake many business valuations in considering the value of the land, of tenancies and of the assets in the business including livestock, machinery, growing and harvested crops, the value of improvements and fixtures for end tenancy claims, and valuations for such purposes as partnership dissolution, taxation and divorce.

9.2   It has less often had to contemplate the valuation of a farming business as an entity in the way that a value might be put on another manufacturing, retail or service business.

9.3   Such issues arise where a tenant's improvements and fixtures are to be valued at their value to an incoming tenant, essentially a partial valuation for a business while a value can be placed on a tenant's farming business for compulsory purchase, when – as in *Wakerley v St Edmundsbury Borough Council* – this can be seen to have been recognised on a loss of profits basis, alongside a separate consideration of a value for the agricultural tenancy. With compulsory purchase providing some of the examples illustrating for this work, it is considered in the closing section of this chapter.

9.4   This might not necessarily be a formal valuation but be an assessment of:
  – where value lies in the business
  – with whom it lies
  – what might increase or support that value
  – what might reduce or jeopardise it
that could all be part of reviewing a business and help advise it in moving forward.

9.5   Such an assessment might be required when considering the sale or purchase of a business or an interest in a business but could equally be for purposes including:
  – restructuring a business
  – lending/borrowing or investment
  – taxation
  – legal purposes
  – divorce
  – compulsory purchase

9.6   The rarity of the use of a business valuation approach in farming situations has been for several reasons, not all of which might hold to the same extent in the future. Those reasons include:
  – the dominance of the values of the assets
  – the dependence of the business on the individuals involved who would not typically transfer with the business, so leaving just the assets
  – farming businesses overwhelmingly being in non-transferrable business structures with only a minority (albeit often larger businesses) run by companies with shares that might require valuation even where their disposal is limited by the company's Articles.
  – farming's specialisation in commodity production has meant there has usually been little of intangible value such as goodwill, brands or intellectual property to assess
  – the usual awkwardness and fiscal disadvantage for a farming or landowning family of holding land and buildings within a company.

9.7   Not only might some of the factors change but the techniques of business valuation may be relevant tools of assistance in appraising farm businesses in the way discussed below, whether or not they are actually structured as company. This could see the assessment of the relative overall business values that could result from different options as to future strategy. That may call for a clear analysis distinguishing between:

- the market value of an interest – that is the expectation as to its value in the open market on the conventional definition
- the fair value for an interest in the context of a particular transaction between specific parties taking account of their interests and motives
- the fair value that might be required for accounting purposes under Financial Reporting Standards
- the worth of an interest – this is the specific value it may have to an individual with particular criteria for holding it or wanting it.

9.8   Interesting questions have arisen for some valuers when considering the value of companies that are actively farming as well as of property investment companies, sometimes for sale or other purposes but more often to assess an individual's shareholding. They may often be close companies with only limited opportunities for share transfer, with the value of shareholding varying with its capacity to control the company, prevent its liquidation or simplify receive dividends.

9.9   Intangible Value: Goodwill – The evolution of some farming businesses in response to the economic pressures foreseen (and seeking the opportunities in that) might start creating value in addition to the underlying assets. Companies may become seen as more useful if they focus on operational farming rather than land holding, with the opportunities to manage family and key staff interests through shareholdings that do not touch on the land and enable flexibility in the proportions held and rights given.

9.10   That may come to see the need in some more specialist farming cases or where the business added value or trades on reputation to assess goodwill, described by the House of Lords as:

"the benefit and advantage of the good name, reputation and connection of a business. It is an attractive force which brings in custom …" (*IRC v Muller and Co's Margarine Ltd*)

9.11   International Financial Reporting Standards is less crisp in defining goodwill as: "an asset representing the future economic benefits arising from other assets acquired in a business combination that are not individually identified and separately recognised". (IFRS 3)

Where there is goodwill, it would be an asset of the business for its balance sheet and when valued on an acquisition is the margin by which the value paid exceeds the assets of the business. It is seen as independent of other intangible assets which are identifiable such as a technology controlled by the business or, while perhaps hard to distinguish in the real world, a strong customer base (the value at issue for Entrepreneurs' Relief in *Gilbert*).

9.12   In practical terms, where a business is being sold or moved it can matter whether the goodwill inheres in:

- a location or a particular individual's skills or contacts that are not readily transferrable (sometimes called "dog goodwill" to reflect loyalty to a person; even "rabbit goodwill") where the location is key) or
- can move with the location or ownership of the business, and are independent of any individuals ("cat goodwill" following the company as it moves)

9.13   Where relevant, it might be valued by identifying the extent to which the average annual profit exceeds what might ordinarily be expected as profit from a business without that extra quality and apply an agreed years' purchase figure to that super-profit.

9.14   A Company Tenancy – Consideration has been given in the CAAV publication, *Valuation of Agricultural Tenancies*, to the valuation of a company holding a non-assignable agricultural tenancy but few other assets, making that tenancy effectively transferrable by sale of the company, resulting occasionally in market evidence. However, the discussion here focuses on companies and other businesses that are active commercial vehicles.

9.15   Other Intangible Assets – Those most commonly met in a farming context will now be payment entitlements (and previously milk quota and livestock premium rights) for which ready market evidence exists.

9.16   Transactions in Companies and Shares – There are openly reported share prices for companies listed on the various stock markets, the complete purchase of such companies is often at a premium or discount to the market value of the issued shares, sometimes because possible synergies in markets, technologies or cost savings may be seen by one or more possible acquirers.

9.17   There is, though, less knowledge of transaction prices for smaller private businesses, let alone an understanding of the specific terms of the transaction or all the relevant factors that informed that price. Not only is this, therefore, likely to be less precise for smaller enterprises such as farming businesses but the agricultural and rural world sees almost none of those transactions giving no direct evidence.

9.18   One important distinction is between the value of the business as a whole and the value of any individual's shareholding in it. The former point is considered in this section and the later in the next (with the specific position where an agricultural tenancy is the major asset considered further in *Valuation of Agricultural Tenancies*.

9.19   These issues are developed in more detail in next two chapters.

10. APPROACHES TO VALUING A BUSINESS

10.1 Approaches to Valuing a Business

10.1.1 Depending on the purpose and the problem, there are a number of ways that can be used to determine a value for a business as a commercial entity.

10.1.2 A key point is that as with other valuation work, values expected to be attributed in the market concern the value available for the future. The past performance is only evidence to be given greater or lesser weight as may be judged appropriate in helping assess what might be paid for future. The value of a business lies in what can be done with it at the valuation date and in its future.

10.1.3 Much of the detailed thinking on business valuation has come from North America where litigation has provided a discipline in developing arguments. That has, however, tended to promote computational analysis with less room for the judgment of circumstance that, with its nuances, can be harder to outline in court. The result can be a reliance on arithmetic rather than opinion with the risks of being precisely wrong, untempered by real appraisal. To an extent the nature of litigation, dealing with past events retrospectively with the greater range of evidence and understanding that may have become available, might sometimes shield such cases from the realities of a contemporaneous valuation of a business

10.1.4 The methods used can be seen to fall into two broad classes of approach:
- "static" approaches based on asset values
- "dynamic" approaches based on profitability.

10.1.5 Static approaches can be criticised as not taking into account the prospect of profit, how the business might be expected to develop or the possibility of liabilities as yet uncrystallised. The first two points can be answered in some cases where asset values already reflect the market's view of future prospects; the third by closer scrutiny of the business, validating its assertions. However and where relevant, they offer a practical advantage of using readily available figures and that the possible adjustments discussed below are usually feasible.

10.1.6 The so-called dynamic approaches might themselves be criticised for working from present profitability which might, in reality, give less information about future than may be given, on occasion, by asset values. The choice of multiplier or discount rate is inherently subjective and, in a low interest rate environment, can make the outcome sensitive to quite small differences.

10.1.7 Those observations simply point to the important of experience in the sector, judgment and perspective with as close an understanding of the business as possible. Despite the arithmetical techniques, this is not simply an exercise in arithmetic which is only a tool to assist analysis and judgment.

10.1.8 The choice of method or the judgment applied in balancing the outcomes of different methods may turn on the type of dispute and the availability of evidence.

10.1.9 Gaining Information and Understanding – The valuer will need as close an understanding of the business as possible, securing as much relevant information as can be gleaned and testing it. This will include the accounts but also an understanding of the business, its approach, the drivers of its value and the risks to it, internal as well as external.

10.1.10 Potential categories of information for this include:
- the nature of the business with its history and outlook
- its ownership including what is owned, how the ownership is structured, why that structure is in place, the existence of any Persons with Significant Control and the motives of the owners
- its management team with its capabilities and, where not the owners, terms of engagement
- factors affecting the legal, financial and actual control of the business
- its place in the supply chain with key suppliers and customers
- the accounts, budgets and other management information, including benchmarking
- its access to capital
- limitations on the business.

10.1.11 There may be particular issues that intervene such as disputes over ownership of the business which might not be relevant to the "intrinsic" value of the business (though the consequences of any associated distraction may be a point to recognise in analysing the accounts) but compromise what the market will pay for the business if the issue is not resolved.

10.1.12 What Does the Company Do? – What are the activities of the business? What risks confront it? Who are its customers, suppliers and competitors? Is it dependent on one product, supplier or customer? When might it need to re-invest and how might that be funded?

10.1.13 What is the Company's Trading Record and Prospects? – The trading value of a company largely lies in its future prospects, the earnings that are to come. Within limitations, past performance as revealed by accounts at least gives a track record and starting point.

10.1.14 Does the company have strength in the market place?

10.1.15 Allied to that are questions as to its capacity in delivering budgets and plans as potential measures of both its management and its place in the market.

10.1.16 Closer analysis could review:
- its ability to generate cash
- return on capital employed
- the scale of borrowings and their cost
- whether working capital is adequate
- the existence of surplus assets
- contingent liabilities or assets.

10.1.17 The Effects of the Economy on the Company – How is the company affected by wider economic factors such as inflation, interest rates or exchange rates? Is it vulnerable to the business cycle or political regulation? Is it influenced by export or import markets? Does it depend on scarce labour? What are the other external constraints?

10.1.18 How Does the Company Sit in its Industry? – Is the overall market changing? How large a share does the company have? Is this a sector of many small firms or dominate by a few large ones?

10.1.19 What is the Quality of Management? – Is the management strong? How good is financial control? Does the company innovate?

10.1.20 The Shares – What restrictions apply to them? What voting rights do they have?

10.2   The Importance of Liquidity

10.2.1   One important question is the extent to which the value of a business, interests in it or its assets is liquid: that is, can be readily converted into cash. A strong, solvent business or valuable property can still be illiquid if its nature or market circumstances makes it hard to sell and requires a long time to sell. That may directly affect its value and its use as security for borrowings.

10.2.2   While government debt and shares in large quoted companies can usually be readily sold, one extreme counter-example is the non-assignable agricultural tenancy which can have substantial value that is usually very hard to realise.

10.2.3   For any level of other risks, a more liquid asset will tend to be valued more highly than a less liquid one. It will typically have lower costs in effecting transactions and be traded faster, that in itself reducing exposure to risk.

10.2.4   As will be noted in the discussion below of business valuation for divorce, the relative liquidity of assets can be important to the final settlement.

10.3   Static Approaches

10.3.1   These essentially work from the asset base of the business. These are likely:
   – to be used for loss-making companies with no prospect of future profits
   – to be more apt where the value left once the owner has gone is likely only to be its assets as is typically the case with farming commodity production businesses and those added value businesses that depend heavily on the individual owner's specialist skills or reputation with little of extra value for the purchaser to take to if the owner leaves
   – where the business holds substantial non-business assets with disproportionate value.

10.3.2   Book Value – This is simply the value of the financial balance sheet, in effect a "melt down" value but with proper, unconstrained marketing of the business.

One advantage of that, if assessed accurately, for the small family businesses that dominate farming and rural life is that it does effectively remove assessment of the individuals who are unlikely to be part of any arms' length transfer of the business. That might though leave a question when considering transfers of parts of the business between those individuals.

10.3.3   That has the problem of how those assets have been assessed. Especially for farming businesses, the balance sheet may record the value of any land in the business at historic acquisition cost, not at its current market value. That market value could, in some cases, recognise not only movements in agricultural land values but reflect any significant hope value for possible non-agricultural uses that the market would take into account.

10.3.4   The assets register underlying the balance sheet offers a check list of the assets to be considered but the valuer should be prepared for other assets to be found. One potential example is where public policy has created an asset, such as payment entitlements (or previously milk quota), after the business was created. While they may have some value, the fact of initial allocation may man they are not recognised. More substantially, it may yet prove in a case that land not shown on the accounts is a partnership asset.

10.3.5 More generally:
- it may ignore intangible assets which for matters such as goodwill, brands and intellectual property can be hard to assess robustly. Historically unimportant for farming businesses, this would again though have ignored the value of any milk quota or, of lesser significance as to capital value, any entitlements to CAP direct payments that had been initially allocated to the business. Goodwill might be harder to realise on a company break-up than a brand or intellectual property
- as the example of entitlements and brand/goodwill value suggest, it is not directly related to the income earning potential of the business
- it might not directly consider future financial costs to the business or other adjustments properly needed to bring balance sheet items to a relevant value.

10.3.6 The depreciation recorded in the accounts, whether for accounting conventions or taxation purposes, might not truly reflect the current actual value of an asset. While buildings will have become part of the land, machinery may have a higher or lower value that recorded in the balance sheet while stocktaking on the basis of cost may leave value to be released.

10.3.7 It is also important to establish that liabilities have been as fully recognised as assets.

10.3.8 Adjusted Book Value – With the issues identified, this follows a reappraisal of the current values of the assets and liabilities in the balance sheet, so correcting for such matters as an under-reporting of the value of the land in the business or where other balance sheet values are overstated.

10.3.9 Liquidation Value – Perhaps most relevant for insolvency and equivalent proceedings, this is the value after deducting the costs of liquidation the business. It could be important to understand if the assets are to be valued on a simple market value basis or with the assumption of a forced sale.

10.3.10 Replacement Value – This uses the costs of replacing the assets (often the fixed assets) in the business. While that would use a current value for land (subject to a view as to whether this is a practical concept for farmland), it has the problem of assessing the cost of replacing equipment that is part way through its life – as with a building that is 10 years old.

10.3.11 Enterprise Value – This rather different approach, probably rarely relevant in a rural context, is based on the cost of funding the business, especially where it has taken on large borrowings, as to fund expansion whether by growth or acquisition. This approach adds:
- the combined value of the shares and
- the value of debt, excluding working capital such as creditors
and then subtracting the value of liquid assets. This calls for care in analysis as, for example, if EBITDA is used to assess the capitalisation of a business it might then be double counting to add back interest bearing liabilities.

10.3.12 A value per share can be given by dividing that total by the number of shares.

10.4 Dynamic Approaches

10.4.1 The "dynamic" approaches to the valuation of a company are based on the expectation of earning income from the business – normally the point of a business – and a view on the security of that income. The assets of the company are, on that assumption, locked within it making its general value to shareholder owners a function of the income it is expected to yield them. That leads to a conventional income-based valuation, as always with a cross check of whether the result looks like one that someone could be expected to pay. The earnings to be considered would be the residual profit after business outgoings, including tax and dividends on preference shares. That would then be capitalised with adjustments as appropriate.

10.4.2 This could be seen as the approach taken in *Wakerley* where five years profits were the assessed compensation for the disturbance/loss of the tenant's farming business and the asset base (the value of the tenancy) formed a separate claim. (For owner-occupied farms, case law has taken the view that the land value encompasses such issues.)

10.4.3 This would conventionally be based on the concept of maintainable earnings, assessed from the company's accounts and assessed in the light of expectations as to future performance and risks, not simply carrying past figures forward. That may reveal trends.

10.4.4 That review includes an appraisal of costs. In particular for a family owned company, it may be necessary to consider what would be the costs of management if done by third parties. Family owners may cost more or less than that figure.

10.4.5 Allowance should be made non-recurring costs and income as well as any particular accounting policies.

10.4.6 A view has to be taken of the life of the business. What prospects does it have?

10.4.7 A real challenge in looking at small businesses is how far the business would survive the present owner leaving: what would be left? Obviously of direct relevance to a transfer of the business, a lender might also be cautious on this point as the loan might be justified where the ownership continues might not be thought secure otherwise.

10.4.8 The simple approach of applying a multiplier to net profit may overlook a view on the prospects for future earnings or the factors that may affect the multiplier, many concerning the security to be attributed to the net profit as when the figure available is higher or lower than might be expected, issues around the financing of the business, the state of the balance sheet, the quality of its contracts and relations with customers and suppliers.

10.4.9 More generally, within any sector, factors to be considered might include:
- the stability and history of the business
- whether it depends on special skills and
- the suitability of its location and premises
- any dependence on special relationships or permissions
- quality of management available to a purchaser
- the reputation of the business
- the level of competitiveness in the sector
- dependences on technology, licences or other factors.

10.4.10 The capitalisation rate, sometimes the price/earnings ratio (P/E ratio), crystallises the market's view as the company's growth potential, its risks and other market or financial circumstances looking ahead. This is a valuation decision calling for careful judgment. Where a ratio is available from apparently comparable transactions, adjustments are likely to be needed for differences in characteristics. Where only one comparable is available, the lack of wider perspective may unduly skew the view here. In some sectors there may be conventional figures for this but careful consideration should be given as to how they should be adjusted for the specific circumstances of the business as well as whether the final answer appears sensible.

10.4.11 Quoted companies may have higher ratios because of their greater liquidity and strength in the marketplace. The ratio may be reduced to reflect problems with the marketability of shares or in access to capital, typically by at least 20 per cent.

10.4.12 There may be a premium for a controlling shareholding.

10.4.13 Discounted Cash Flow – In producing a capital value from an income measure, the choice of the discount rate needs a judgment of the value of money over time with the risks posed to that income. Clear analysis will be needed to understand how far and which risks are being considered and allowed for in the projected cash flows and, alternatively, in the discount rate.

10.4.14 The more developed forms of this approach are more likely to be relevant to larger businesses possibly less vulnerable to variation in the figures. This may use three variables:
- expected net income to be yielded by the business, usually looked at as net or free cash flow but needing the valuer to feel assured as the soundness of its assessment, with adjustment for extraordinary items and easing comparison with preceding and future years. A potential need for reinvestment (as where present technology or machinery is aging) might need to be allowed for, reducing the prospective net income. Typically, net income will be assessed for small businesses before taxation. If the net income figure is misstated, that error will be factored through the calculation and so this is likely to lead to using an Adjusted Net Income figure. A particular factor for small businesses can be the level of remuneration and benefits drawn by the owner
- any expectations of growth rates or retrenchment for the business, a point that can be more subjective still. The more that this can be sustained from the evidence of the market, the better
- the cost of capital.

It is essentially a valuation based on the business itself without reference to values for other businesses save in so far as they may assist with identifying the discount rate to be used to create capital value.

10.4.15 If working out this assessment over a limited time horizon, say five or seven years, a value should then usually be attributed to what will then be there after that, perhaps by taking a view of its prospective fair value balance sheet and discounting back to the present.

10.4.16 The apparent arithmetical precision of the technique should not prompt the illusion that the answer is necessarily accurate. It should always be subject a sense check as to whether that value would actually be paid.

10.4.17 Comparison with Relevant Market Indicators – This tends to draw on wider market knowledge with the use of multipliers observed from review of potentially comparable businesses and an understanding of the sector. This might use such a rule of thumb as a price/earnings (P/E) ratio.

10.5   A Dividends Basis

10.5.1 As reviewed below, where the only value expected from shares lies in the dividends they may yield, particularly typical for minority shareholdings when the company is unlikely to be broken up for its assets, then their valuation is of that income stream.

10.5.2 In simple terms, that:
– takes the expected stream of dividends – requiring an assessment of the maintainable dividends per share
– divides it by a rate of retrain that the investor would expect from other assets with comparable prospects as to growth, risk and liquidity.

10.5.3 Notional Dividends? – Sometimes, profitable companies have had a policy of not paying a dividend but rather retaining earnings in the business of which the shareholder still has ownership. That might be commercially justified where it enables more investment or expansion with a view to future profits or to help clear expensive debt. Such strategies might pave the way to larger dividends in the future or create a more saleable company.

10.5.4 One speculative approach occasionally adopted, according to a view of the circumstances and reasons for not paying a dividend, is to hypothesise a dividends policy and capitalise the notional income stream deduced, probably with discount for the uncertainty involved.

10.6   Review

10.6.1 Especially in the circumstances likely to be met by agricultural valuers, the outcome of this analysis might, with the issues around the arithmetic involved, be best taken as indicative, requiring both judgment is determining an opinion as to value where this is needed and care in reporting and explanation.

10.6.2 Nonetheless, these approaches can also give the tools to help judge the relative outcomes in terms of value from different possible approaches.

11. VALUING PARTNERSHIPS, BUSINESSES AND SHARES

11.1 Valuation and Partnerships

11.1.1 A valuation may be needed of:
- a partnership business as whole, as if it is to be sold as a whole business
- an interest in a partnership, as where a partner is being paid out by the continuing partners. In that circumstance, this payment may be simply based on the recorded current and capital accounts unless the partnership agreement makes other provision or the outgoing partner can negotiate a different basis. For a farming partnership, the difference between the balance sheet and actual values for farmland may be material here.

11.1.2 As elsewhere, the value of a partnership may be different from the net asset value recorded in its balance sheet as it may need to take account of unrealised values in property (such as farmland that may be shown at an historic value), goodwill (still rare in farming context but possible for some diversification) and other matters.

11.1.3 The conventional approach to valuing a partnership or an interest in one starts by considering the net assets as shown on the balance sheet. If this is not being done as at a year-end, this will need to be updated.

11.1.4 There may then need to be a valuation of the overall business, prepared on a similar basis to that reviewed above for a company, considering:
- income, costs and profits
- assets
- future prospects
- comparable transactions
- expectations and conventions in the relevant sector.

11.1.5 Particularly for family partnerships, the accounts may need adjustment costs or liabilities as well as assets that are personal, rather than business, in nature. Any provision for Income Tax will also need to be treated in this way as it is a personal liability.

11.1.6 Once a value of a whole partnership is arrived at, an individual partner's share can be assessed on the basis of the profit-sharing ratios (unless the agreement imposes any other basis).

11.1.7 When assessing a partner's share, it is less usual to reduce its proportionate value of the whole by a discount as the starting point is that each partner can force a dissolution. That may be tempered by the partnership agreement or circumstances.

11.1.8 Where being assessed for a divorce, the value of a partnership interest should then be reduced for any liability to Capital Gains Tax on that disposal.

11.2 Consideration of Partnerships

11.2.1 It can be harder than might be thought to establish the facts of a partnership. The starting point is to review the partnership agreement (if there is one) but then consider how its terms may:
- have been varied over time by behaviour
- have been varied over time by agreement
- where it is incomplete and so governed by the default terms of the 1890 Act.

Indeed, where the partnership agreement did not make provisions, it could be that any formal agreement that is available was anyway terminated by a then partner's death, with that agreement now simply being evidence as to what the current terms might be.

11.2.2   The agreement should identify:
  – who·the partners were at the date of the agreement
  – the proportions in which they are to share profits and losses
  – their entitlements to capital
  – partnership property
  – the accounting period and arrangements
  – the duration of the partnership and how it might be dissolved
  – provisions for the retirement of partners
  – their entitlements, liabilities and rights on dissolution (including whether one partner can buy another partner's interests so as to be able continue the underlying enterprise).

11.3   What is in the Business? – Warnings from Partnerships

11.3.1   It may often not be clear as to what assets are actually held by a business. This can be particularly an issue where the interests of the owners and the business have not been kept properly separate or adequately distinguished from each other leaving in a fog of overlapping entities.

11.3.2   Indeed, one possibility is that an asset, such as an area of farmland, is the personal property of one of the family members, often also a partner, but leased to the partnership which then has an interest in it, especially significant if it is a tenancy under the 1986 or 1991 Acts.

11.3.3   As well as posing issues between the partners, that can then have taxation consequences and land that is partnership property can qualify for full Business Property Relief (BPR) from Inheritance Tax, material where there is development value that would not be covered by Agricultural Property Relief, while land that is owned by one partner but used by the partnership might only qualify for 50 per cent BPR. That distinction may also be relevant to the treatment of the land for Entrepreneurs' Relief from Capital Gains Tax, where land that only used by the partnership would fall under the rules for associated disposals with possible reductions in relief.

11.3.4   As illustrated by many cases, the long history of partnership disputes shows that inadequate or no documentation, possibly shifting attitudes and the passage of time can leave the status or valuation of land or other assets used by the partnership at issue. Where such cases reach the courts, they are to be decided on the available facts, evidence and arguments, often conflicting; sometimes, only the accounts are available as evidence and they too may be unclear.

11.3.5   Failing these, the Partnership Act says at s.20(1):
"All property and rights and interests in property originally brought into the partnership stock or acquired, whether by purchase or otherwise, on account of the firm, or for the purposes and in the course of the partnership business, are called in this Act partnership property, and must be held and applied by the partners exclusively for the purposes of the partnership and in accordance with the partnership agreement."

11.3.6   In *Wild v Wild*, the question before the court in 2018 was whether Beard Hall Farm in Derbyshire had, during the history of the family's dealings with each other, become an asset of the partnership (which only had an oral agreement), and so to be taken into account on dissolution, or not. The note in the 1989 fixed assets register of "property: £40,750" was held to refer to the farm but while "likely to be very powerful and persuasive evidence but it is not conclusive of that question". After reviewing much conflicting and confused evidence and recollection, the judge concluded that the farm (now £1.4 million) was not a partnership asset.

11.3.7   In *Ham v Bell* the court had to consider:
- whether farmland (with the farmhouse) that had been an asset of a preceding partnership was property of the replacement partnership including another family member or whether its inclusion in the accounts for the early years of the new partnership was an accounting error that had then been corrected in later accounts. The court found that, on the facts of the case (at one point considering the drafting of the parents' wills), the land and house were assets of the new partnership
- within that, the situation where the partnership had rent free access to the farmland but met the cost of improvements to it, a point that might also arise for a company or other structure. Following the decision on a mining partnership *Burdon v Barkus*, the court held that such actions did not make the land an asset of that partnership but might be considered in the financial settlement between the partners (with principles set out in the farming case *Davies v H&R Ecroyd Ltd*).

11.3.8   Other issues can arise where new assets are created during the life of the partnership. Thus, *Faulks v Faulks* had to consider whether, on the facts of that partnership, milk quota, created on a particular legal basis by the EU after the commencement of the partnership, was a partnership asset or not.

11.3.9   That reasoning was later followed in *Davies v H&R Ecroyd Ltd* where the land was not a partnership asset and so the milk quota, in so far it was seen to be associated with land, would not be one either.

11.3.10 In *Ham v Ham* (resulting from *Ham v Bell*) the Court of Appeal had to consider whether a partnership agreement's requirement that assets be valued on dissolution at "net value" without defining or explaining it, meant at book value or at market value – the land was in the accounts at historic cost. Weighing difficult arguments – in a context where the exiting partner triggering the matter had introduced no capital and the resulting payment could force the sale of the farm – the court found that it meant market value.

11.4   Shares in a Business

11.4.1   Other than a sole trader a business may have more than one owner, whether as partners in an unincorporated business or as shareholders in a company. If the business has value then a share in the ownership of the business may have value, potentially requiring appraisal and valuation. This is not necessarily a proportionate share of the asset value.

11.4.2   For the businesses typically met by agricultural valuers, there is no wider market for shares in partnerships or companies, with these usually held only by some family members. As with statutorily protected agricultural tenancies that does not rob of them of value but can make that harder to determine and realise. Much may turn on the purpose of the valuation which may include:
- business transactions between the parties
- succession
- taxation
- litigation
- acquisition and disposal.

11.4.3   However, these structures can also be a means to operate specialist ventures which may need or warrant the participation in the business of a third party's skill or outside equity. Indeed, a share in the business or increasing that share can be a reward for success. Save where directly focussed on property development and use, such ventures might only rarely include land as an asset of the business.

11.4.4   Professional practices that are structured as partnerships, more often with otherwise unconnected parties, need a means to value what is needed for new partners to enter and retired partners to withdraw, so here providing an exit route at the value then available.

11.5   What is a "Share" in Partnership?

11.5.1   While a partner's interest in a partnership may be referred to as a share in the partnership, it is not of the same nature as a shareholding in a company which can (subject to the company's articles and market circumstances) be transferred or sold for value to a third party.

11.5.2   Its nature was outlined by the Court of Appeal's decision in *Popat v Schonchhatra*:

> "Although it is both customary and convenient to speak of a partner's "share" of the partnership assets, that is not a truly accurate description of his interest in them, at all events so long as the partnership is a going concern. While each partner has a proprietary interest in each and every asset, he has no entitlement to any specific asset and, in consequence, no right, without the consent of the other partners or partner, to require the whole or even a share of any particular asset to be vested in him. On dissolution the position is in substance not much different, the partnership property falling to be applied, subject to sections 40 to 43 (if and so far as applicable), in accordance with sections 39 and 44 of the 1890 Act. As part of that process, each partner in a solvent partnership is presumptively entitled to payment of what is due from the firm to him in respect of capital before division of the ultimate residue in the shares in which profits are divisible; see section 44 (b) 3. and 4. It is only at that stage that a partner can accurately be said to be entitled to a share of anything, which, in the absence of agreement to the contrary, will be a share of cash."

11.6   Valuation of Shares in a Partnership

11.6.1   As a partnership is a mutual association, there is no arm's length trade in partnership shares. A partner's share only has value in itself and as between that partner and the other partners, taking account of the expected life of the partnership under its agreement or the law.

11.6.2   The default rule under the Partnership Act 1890, subject to the terms of the partnership agreement, is that where a partner leaves or dies, the partnership is dissolved with the assets released. The position for partnership property is then as stated in s.39:

> "On the dissolution of a partnership every partner is entitled, as against the other partners in the firm, and all persons claiming through them in respect of their interests as partners, to have the property of the partnership applied in payment of the debts and liabilities of the firm, and to have the surplus assets after such payment applied in payment of what may be due to the partners respectively after deducting what may be due from them as partners to the firm; and for that purpose any partner or his representatives may on the termination of the partnership apply to the Court to wind up the business and affairs of the firm."

11.6.3   As shown in a number of court decisions where the position has been unclear to at least one partner, what constitutes partnership property will be a matter of the agreement and the evidence (often in the partnership accounts), including the behaviour of the parties.

11.6.4   Shares in a partnership may have different rights to capital and to income, potentially useful where new partners are being introduced and others take a lesser role. Those differences in rights would be relevant to the attribution of value to any one partnership share, with the approach to capital based on a share in the net assets and to income on the expectation of income claims on the partnership for its likely duration.

11.6.5   The Partnership Act specifically intervenes where one partner assigns or charges their partnership share. S.31(1) states that in such case, the assignee is not entitled
> "… during the continuance of the partnership, to interfere in the management or administration of the partnership business or affairs, or to require any accounts of the partnership transactions, or to inspect the partnership books"

but is entitled:
> "only to receive the share of profits to which the assigning partner would otherwise be entitled, and the assignee must accept the account of profits agreed to by the partners."

On the dissolution of the partnership, s.31(2) then provides that:
> "the assignee is entitled to receive the share of the partnership assets to which the assigning partner is entitled as between himself and the other partners, and, for the purpose of ascertaining that share, to an account as from the date of the dissolution."

11.7   Valuing Shares in a Company

11.7.1   While shares in quoted companies can be readily valued from the financial press or other sources, it may prove impossible to find market evidence of sales of shares in the small companies, typically close companies, being discussed here, often subject to limitations as to whom shares can be transferred. There may, though. be occasional market evidence of the sales of 100 per cent shareholdings in companies holding farm tenancies, particularly at times of agricultural prosperity.

11.7.2   In reviewing this subject, HMRC has for its taxation purposes regarding Inheritance Tax and Capital Gains Tax a Shares Valuation Division with its own in house manual setting out its views on the relevant legislation, approaches and issues which can be seen at: https://www.gov.uk/hmrc-internal-manuals/shares-and-assets-valuation-manual

11.7.3   There is no standard methodology with much turning on facts, circumstances and the availability of evidence. It may, occasionally, be that there is actual evidence from a recent share sale, other review (but taking account of its purpose) or an offer to buy the company (whether accepted or not).

11.7.4   The principle is then to consider the value on the basis of the assumptions required for market value, that value expected on standard assumptions between willing parties. The characteristics of the shares would have to be considered, including any restrictions on their sale and the influence of that shareholding on the management of the company.

11.7.5   A loss-making company might, in the absence of better future prospects, be valued solely on its break-up value after associated costs (and have regard to such tax as might be due on any capital gains then arising). However, a valuation for divorce purposes might have to assess the causes of any recent move into losses and whether and how they might be turned round.

11.7.6 The approach to be taken turns on the proportion of the shares involved. Different scales of shareholding offer different opportunities under the Companies Act to the shareholder with respect to the company and so to the tenancy and the business based on the tenancy. The Companies Act 2006 provides that:
- a special resolution requires the support of not less than 75 per cent of the voting rights exercised (s.283)
- ordinary resolutions must be passed by a majority.

The practical effect is that the dissolution of a company requires control of 75 per cent of the shares but operational management control 50 per cent. A shareholding of less than 25 per cent cannot by itself block dissolution.

11.7.7 As a result, there may be a premium value for a shareholding that gives control of a company, that premium being likely to turn on what additional value that control may unlock, whether through improving the performance of the business or for other factors. Shares that lack control may have values discounted according to their circumstances, including the ability to influence management. Limitations on the marketability of shares may impose discounts on their valuations.

11.7.8 Where the shareholding is 75 per cent or greater, the notional purchaser of that shareholding can liquidate the company. That gives access to the asset value base so far as that is realisable but there are basic obligations to minority shareholdings. The valuer should take account of the liability to Corporation Tax on gains made on the liquidation of the company which is then by definition not a going concern. However, if working from the company's earnings leads to a higher value then that would be used instead.

11.7.9 Where, at the other extreme, the shareholding is 25 per cent or less, then the holder has insufficient shares on his own to prevent the other shareholder(s) from winding-up the company or passing a special resolution. This shareholding could usually be assessed on its potential to earn income through dividends. The value of the assets might not be directly relevant and so it would usually be wrong to follow a net asset value approach. A valuation of the underlying assets, whether land or machinery, is unlikely to be appropriate unless there are significant prospects of the company being taken over or being liquidated.

11.7.10 A shareholding of less than 10 per cent cannot resist a general meeting being called at short notice.

11.7.11 Where the shareholding falls between 51 per cent and 75 per cent, the purchaser of that shareholding would have managing control but cannot terminate the tenancy single-handed and will have obligations to minority shareholders. The bid of a speculative purchaser would be geared to anticipated profit or any assumed potential route to achieve liquidation. For shareholdings in this range, the extent to which the underlying assets are relevant could turn on the share transfer restrictions and the identity, age and health of the other shareholders.

11.7.12 Where the shareholding is between 25 per cent and 49 per cent, the approach would turn on the balance, distribution and circumstances of the other significant shareholdings. It may be that a valuation should be based on the earning potential of the shares. The dividend policy may well be such as to exclude dividends as a basis for valuation. Earnings may be variable and accounting profits are after directors' remuneration, suggesting that a valuation higher than one based on income seems inappropriate.

11.7.13 There appears to be very little, if any, market evidence of sales of partial (even controlling) shareholdings in family farming companies – a point which suggests that they are unattractive deals for both hypothetical purchasers and hypothetical vendors.

11.7.14 The sale of a 100 per cent shareholding delivers a complete transfer of the company and can be seen, subject to any circumstances as tantamount to a transfer of the full value of the company, however that is best assessed.

11.7.15 Discounts for Partial Shareholdings – A Special Commissioner case, *McArthur*, has reviewed the discounts to net asset value to be applied to shareholdings of various sizes in unquoted companies. While in each case, something may turn on the specific facts, the decision awarded:
- the 12.5 per cent discount sought by the Revenue for shareholdings of 51.1 per cent and 69.9 per cent. The Revenue's argument was based in part on *Goldstein v Levy* and was in respect of lack of marketability
- a 45 per cent discount for a 26.8 per cent shareholding, arrived at allowing a 25 per cent discount perceived for quoted investment and property companies, less a further 50 percent for lack of marketability but with the resulting 37.5 per cent enhanced by a half to reflect its potential nuisance value to those managing the business (following *Re Lynall*).
- a 65 per cent discount for an 8.16 per cent shareholding as it was too small to have such a nuisance value.

11.7.16 That can be seen to have analogies with the varying discounts for minority undivided shares in property determined in *Charkham*,

11.7.18 The decision in *Cash and Carry v Inspector of Taxes* considered a 24 per cent shareholding in an unquoted company that had been liquidated after many years of not paying dividends. In these circumstances, HMRC argued for the larger discount for the percentage shareholding: two thirds as opposed to the taxpayer's proposal of 10 per cent, suggesting that reflected the uncertainties involved. The Special Commissioner determined a deduction of 55 per cent, working from the decision in *Caton's Administrators v Couch (Inspector of Taxes)* where the value of a 14.02 per cent shareholding in a successful company had been discounted by 50 per cent

11.7.19 Where then only shareholders are husband and wife, it would be typical to view the company in a divorce as though it were a partnership, valuing the shares on a pro rata basis without a discount. That might be applied more widely where the shareholders are expected to act in concert at the time of any presumed disposal but that is very much a matter for specific appraisal.

11.8 Issues of Valuation for Businesses in Divorce Cases
11.8.1 Where a divorce concerns a couple of whom at least one has an interest in business, the business becomes a factor in the divorce settlement with view needed as to its value. That business may be a company, partnership or a sole trader.

11.8.2 Farms, with not only property and business aspects as well often the home and with complex family interests, are then especially found to raise particular issues. While limited liquidity and the low return on capital might suggest an order of sale as the answer, courts are reluctant to do this but rather to find that farming cases are "notoriously difficult to resolve" (*R v R (Lump Sum Repayments)*) requiring "creative ingenuity ... if a just and fair result is to be achieved" (*P v P Inherited Property*). At best, case law establishes general principles, rather than binding precedents, as the courts wrestle with difficult circumstances.

11.8.3   The approaches may vary according to whether the partnership only comprises husband and wife or includes at least one other person. As a simple husband and wife business partnership might not typically continue after divorce, the more common possibilities are to:
- allow one partner to take over the partnership business, possibly with the adjustment of a payment or property transfer to the departing spouse
- sell the business as a whole
- dissolve the partnership and wind up the assets.

11.8.4   More complex situation can arise where third parties are involved in a partnership confronted with divorce. The nature of a share in a partnership makes it hard for a court to direct a sale while, on similar grounds, the consent of the other continuing partners would be required for a spouse's share to be used as security to borrow required money. However, the family context of many farming partnerships might offer a little more flexibility in practice.

11.8.5   It could be that where a partnership is to continue after divorce, especially in order to enable the income to meet needs through regular payments, there is no need to value the overall business as its capital value is not being realised. That, in substance, was the approach taken in the company case, *Evans v Evans*:

"Whilst it may be necessary to obtain a broad assessment of the value of a shareholding in a private company it is inappropriate to undertake an expensive and meaningless exercise to achieve a precise valuation of a private company which will not be sold."

11.8.6   That might point to a simpler look at the capital accounts with any adjustment thought needed though the nature of that capital is for review. An illustration of that was a case where the senior partner's capital account in an accountancy practice included a significant element that could not, in reality, be withdrawn from the business. The judge in *N v N (Financial Provision: Sale of Company)* took the view that this need not be in the schedule of assets but would bear its benefit in mind in arriving at his overall decision. That again points to income returns on such capital being a more important factor than the option of the court insisting on the dissolution of a partnership.

11.8.7   That also illustrates the potential willingness of the court to distinguish between liquid and illiquid capital when arriving at an answer. In one case, the Court of Appeal stated:

"It was true that £18,000 [the payment to the wife] was less than a quarter of the husband's capital, but £18,000 cash was one thing and £73,000 unliquid capital was another" (*Dawe v Dawe*).

That case concerned a situation where three brothers had jointly inherited 136 acres, which they farmed through their limited company which rented the land from them. The court indicted that it would only have made an order converting the ownership interest from a tenancy in common into a joint tenancy and make an order for sale if that were the only way to make provision for the wife of one brother.

11.8.8   In *P v P (Financial Provision: Lump Sum)* (see also below), the court noted that:

> "a sum of £100,000 in liquid assets is one thing; £100,000 invested in a small farm in the west country is something very different"

as well as recognising potential Capital Gains Tax and Inheritance Tax, in distinguishing between cash and the lower net value of a property.

11.8.9   Again, it can be important to identify what property is partnership property or is personally owned. If necessary, the court can be asked to determine this with guidance given in *TL v ML* and, with the potential need to join third parties in this, *Fisher Meredith v JH*.

11.8.10 Where reviewing farming accounts, the court has been known in extreme cases to take into consideration evidence of substantial financial mismanagement (more than simply making losses). In *Moorish v Moorish*, the court found that:

> "the husband had been managing the farm in an entirely wasteful way and that the continuation of the business under his management would lead to a progressive reduction of the assets and the farm would have to be sold".

The Court of Appeal distinguished this from making an award of a lump sum that would require the sale of the business.

11.8.12 As well as the assessment needed generally to establish a fair division of assets, issues can include:

  – what is needed for a business to survive, supporting the party involved in it and sustaining any continuing alimony payment by that party. A business and its property may not only have a capital value to be considered but, if not broken up by the settlement, may enable the income from which the future livelihood of one of the parties and continuing payments will be derived. That may require some balancing adjustment to meet fairness. Freehold farmland poses particular a challenge in this with the relatively high ratio between capital value and income
  – valuation of the business before the marriage in identifying what might be within the scope of matrimonial assets, with background issues for farms and estates often complicated by the land often having been an asset of one of the families, commonly involved over several generations.

11.8.13 This may be additionally complicated for a farming business where it includes, perhaps depends on, an agricultural tenancy, especially one under the Agricultural Holdings Act 1986 or the Agricultural Holdings (Scotland) Act 1991. It may be appropriate to consider the value of the tenancy even though realising that value may be rarely feasible and, on occasion, the court can direct the transfer of the tenancy (even if unassignable) between divorcing parties. Such a tenancy may also depreciate the value of the freehold subject to it. Specific approaches to valuation of agricultural tenancies and their application to divorce cases are reviewed in the CAAV's publication, *Valuation of Agricultural Tenancies*.

11.8.14 The Division of Assets – The House of Lords decision in *Miller v Miller* opened noting:

> "that most intractable of problems: how to achieve fairness in the division of property following a divorce"

before reviewing the general principles for the exercise of:

> "the wide discretionary powers conferred on the court by Part II of the Matrimonial Causes Act 1973".

Farms are specifically seen by divorce practitioners as posing particular problems and so often to be "special cases" warranting additional care by those handling divorce cases.

11.8.15 *Charman* considered which property is subject to the sharing rule for assets and ruled that:

"the principle applies to all the parties' property".

Exceptions were allowed for short marriages, dual careers, and agreements between the parties and in addition "to the extent that their property is non-matrimonial, there is likely to be better reason for departure from equality."

11.8.16 The Supreme Court affirmed that basic principle in the farming case, *White v White*, stating that the starting point with divorce cases would be an equal division of assets. However, that was case where husband and wife were also equal partners in the farming partnership, informing the Court of Appeal's view in its decision that:

"In a case where the spouses were in business together, the starting point has to be their respective financial positions at the end of their business relationship. This may in many cases be achieved by a broad assessment of the financial position and I am not advocating a detailed partnership account. At this stage it is not a question of contribution to the family, which is to be found at subsection (2)(f) but of entitlement. Of course, as Ormrod LJ said in *Browne v Pritchard* [1975] 1 WLR 1366, subsection (2)(a) should not be allowed to dominate the picture, but it has, in a suitable case, such as the present appeal, to be given its due weight in the balancing exercise. The partnership case where the wife is found to be an equal partner, even if the assets are large, is in a wholly different category, from the ´big money´ cases such as *Dart v Dart* [1996] 2 FLR 286 or *Conran v Conran* [1997] 2 FLR 615. In the latter cases, the origin of the wealth was clearly on one side and the emphasis was rightly on contribution not entitlement."

That is a question of entitlements under the partnership agreement, not of needs or compensation.

11.8.17 The entitlements basis for that has been illustrated in:

- *AR v AR*, where the farming resources of more than £20 million were substantially owned by the husband and inherited from his father, saw the wife receive £4.3 million, assessed on the basis of her needs only having no entitlement to a share in the business value
- *P v P (Financial Provision: Lump Sum)*, where the wife was the sole owner of farm by gift from her father but the business was carried on as a husband and wife partnership. With the wife keeping the farm and children and the court seeing the husband as having few skills or prospects, she was to make three payments amounting to 15 per cent of the value of the farm.

11.8.18 The probable position for a husband and wife partnership with agreed but unequal shares is that that would be given weight but alongside all other factors as the court exercised its discretion.

11.8.19 That principle may since have been developed or qualified for England and Wales by the Supreme Court decision on pre-nuptial agreements in *Radmacher v Granatino* that, where parties have entered into pre-nuptial agreements, they intend that such agreements should be upheld. While now more discussed in the context of family businesses and, in particular, farms and estates, that still appears to allow a court to waive a pre-nuptial agreement if, for example, it is seen as unfair to children of the marriage.

11.8.20 Scotland – In Scotland, the Family Law (Scotland) Act 1985 at ss. 9 and 10 sets out a statutorily prescribed principle that the parties should share in the value of the 'matrimonial property' (the matrimonial home and property acquired during the marriage otherwise than by gift or inheritance) as distinct from property generally.

11.8.21 In valuing businesses, developing case law illustrates a number of themes.

11.8.22 The valuation giving a range of figures – Valuers are usually expected to give a specific figure making this a matter for the instructions or the court's direction order. In *D v D and B Limited* it was noted that, as there may usually be no ready market in shares in private companies, highly competent valuers using the same methods may still reach very different results as a natural outcome of the judgments and opinions they must form.

11.8.23 Avoiding double counting – Where the prospective value of end of tenancy compensation is considered it should be checked if the value is already shown in some way in the tenant's accounts. More generally, an asset cannot both be available for realisation and continue to yield income.

11.8.24 Discounting the value of minority interests, principally in companies – It was said in *Charman*:

> "... where for instance a case proceeds on the basis that a sale at less than true market value is inevitable to satisfy a likely court order then discounts at high levels are often appropriate. But where a sale can be avoided or delayed to enable full value to be extracted over reasonable time that too must, in fairness, be properly reflected in valuation ... exactly the same kind of considerations apply when looking eg at discounts for valuation of minority interests in private companies. Sometimes they apply, sometimes, especially in family situations, they do not."

11.8.25 Discount to reflect risk – In *Charman*, the wife's share of the asset values was reduced because the assets retained by the husband were seen to be risky.

11.8.26 The Family Proceedings Rules 1991 recognise the need for proportionality (Rule 2.51D) and the farming divorce case *B v B (Financial Provision)* is seen as authority for the proposition that precision in valuation is not required provided both assets and liquidity can be assessed broadly.

11.8.26 In a caution as to trying to assess future values, as might be the case if trying to bring a potential special purchaser into play, the judge in *CR v CR* said when considering the effect possible future growth on share values:

> "if one were to value the shares now on the basis of trying to project forwards into the future then, to be logically fair and consistent, one would have to do that in respect of several of the listed assets, which would signal a descent into forensic chaos."

11.8.27 The taxation implications of any possible transfer or disposal also need to be considered. Capital Gains Tax or Stamp Duty Land Tax may apply to directly to any such disposal and so reduce its net proceeds. The loss of land may also have wider effects as, for example, the assessment of the dwelling as a farmhouse of a character appropriate for Agricultural Property Relief from Inheritance Tax.

11.8.28 This analysis shows the importance of the terms of reference in the instruction letter or the court's direction order. Unless the valuer has secured clear instructions, then the requirements of the Red Book, albeit not necessarily applicable to RICS members for advice to a court, might be seen as leading to a market value approach based only on the period before a notice to quit for alienation took effect. The parties in *A v A* were urged to obtain valuation evidence in a more focussed way and at an earlier stage to avoid the need for a full investigation of the values. The valuer may also be asked to comment on the liquidity and sustainability of the business.

11.8.29 Even where advising one party, the valuer should be conscious of the potential for appointment as an expert witness in the case with the accompanying duties to the court. The court may insist on there being a single joint valuer of the property interests as part of narrowing the issues which it has to decide. In addition to the guidance of the Civil Procedure Rules Part 35 Practice Direction – Experts and Assessors (introduced into divorce cases by the Family Proceedings Rules, rule 2.61C), specific guidance to experts in divorce cases is given by:
- Practice Direction: Ancillary Relief Procedure (2000) 1 FLR 997, and
- Best Practice Guide for Instructing a Single Joint Expert produced by the Ancillary Relief Advisory Committee of the President of the Family Division.

11.8.30 *R v R (Lump Sum Repayments)* [2004] 1 FLR 928 considered a more complex situation. The husband had a 6.18 per cent share in a long established farming company with the prospect of more (but not a majority of) shares on the death of his mother, all with a value of £1.5 million but when discounted as a minority interest assessed at £448,000. The core problem was to find a new house for the wife then occupying a farmhouse when the husband could not readily realise the value underlying the shares. While the balance sheet showed a net value at cost and after depreciation of £851,000, the net value of assets was put at £3.8 million. The answer found was:
- for the wife to buy a house elsewhere
- using mortgage being funded by the husband through monthly payments
- secured by the wife having a first charge over the husband's shares
- leaving the husband with a net annual income of £13,007 (previously £41,309), the modesty of which the court saw as offset by the scale of personal expenses met by the company. That can point to a close review of that aspect of the accounts. It was also noted that, among other specific factors, the husband might have some influence over his future remuneration from the company, the wife would no longer be paid by it, and the occupation value of the farmhouse was released.

11.9   Illustrations from Compulsory Purchase
11.9.1   When is a Business Valued? – Compulsory purchase law has generally taken the view that, for commercial property, the market value of land includes the purchase of the right to make profits from it. Thus, compensation for market value encapsulates the loss of profits:
> "No man would pay for land in addition to its market value the capitalised value of the savings and additional profits which he would hope to make by the use of it" (*Pastoral Finance Association Ltd v The Minister*).

Thus, it was held in *Wimpey & Co v Middlesex County Council* that the company could not claim for both market value of the development land taken and the loss of the development profits they would have had.

11.9.1   That is, though, overridden where the business can be shown to have a value to the claimant over above the value of the land being taken, with the head of claim being variously described as "loss of profits" or "loss of goodwill" and could arise from circumstances such as cancelled or varied contracts or, as in *Bede Distributors Ltd v Newcastle Corporation*, a temporary loss of profits during relocation to new premises.

11.9.2   With the background of the principle of equivalence for compulsory purchase, the basis of valuation is the value to the owner, as the market value basis of Rule 2 is excluded for Rule 6 disturbance (*Afzal v Rochdale MBC*).

11.9.3 While the conventional approach was adopted in *Ryde International plc v London Regional Transport (No 2)*, the Court of Appeal accepted that profits lost as a direct result of the compulsory purchase and not reflected in the market value of land could be compensated. That approach had been seen for a farm tenancy in *Watson v Secretary of State for Air* where the Court of Appeal allowed a disturbance claim for the temporary loss of profit of the crop that was almost ready to harvest but dismissed a claim for the profit on the following year's crop as that should be reflected in the value of interest in the land, saying:

> "If the figure is properly arrived at under Rule (2) it seems to me that any further sum for loss of profits is necessarily excluded, for otherwise he would be having the same thing twice over."

11.9.4 In *Welford v EDF Energy Networks Ltd*, the Court of Appeal accepted that once an owner of land has a business and starts work in that business which proves profitable, compulsory purchase will create disturbance that is not reflected in the market value of that land.

11.9.5 It may be that this claim more readily arises where the dispossessed interest is a tenancy, whether of farmland or other property. Thus, in *Wakerley,* the Lands Tribunal made a clear distinction between the value of the tenancy (awarding a sum of £100 in the absence of evidence) and the value for disturbance including loss of profits (having deducted rent) assessed with a five year multiplier on a 33.5 year expectancy of occupation under the secure tenancy and after deducting rent. The Tribunal and Court of Appeal decisions in *Wakerley* point to the need, when analysing the situation, to be careful to distinguish between the valuation of the business and the valuation of the interest in the land.

11.9.6 In *Reynolds v Manchester City Council*, the Tribunal set out this approach for a one man business:
- determine historic profit, often the average of the last three years
- adjust that by deducting:
    - an allowance for rent (if no rent has been charged), to avoid double counting with the as that would be in the property compensation
    - an allowance for interest on capital
- capitalise that by a multiplier, often between 2 and 5.

11.9.7 For larger business, profit as assessed on an EBITDA basis might be used.

11.9.8 The Example of *Welcocks* – Specific approaches to such a valuation have recently been tested in *Welcocks Skips Limited v Network Rail Infrastructure Limited* . Welcocks operated a waste transfer station and a skip hire and recycling business on land held on four tenancies subject to an acquisition by Network Rail. Two of the tenancies were not contracted out under Part 2 of the Landlord and Tenant Act 1954 and gave rise to this claim. While claim for "shadow losses" (losses from losing trade in advance of acquisition because of its threat) was rejected on the basis of the evidence and arguments put, a claim for business value was upheld.

11.9.9 The valuation of this claim was extensively argued, working from the expected annual profit of the business which had been agreed by expert witnesses on an EBITDA basis at £1.1 million, once the Tribunal had determined the business assumption as to trade with one previously major customer.

11.9.10 Illustrating a variety of approaches and analyses, the arguments were then about how that income figure should be capitalised with reference to:

- **quoted company multiples** (QCMs) – looking at multiples between income and share capitalisation for "broadly comparable" waste management public companies, scale being one factor in identifying the most comparable ones. Adjustments were considered for:
  - relative profitability
  - differences in debt, Welcocks being debt free
  - differences in the services offered by the companies
  - the advantage of closer ownership control and so the sale of all the business rather than some shares
  - the disadvantage of a private company possibly being les easily traded.

The conclusion on these points was a multiplier of 7.

- **comparable transactions multiples** (CTMs) – these came from transactions in other private waste management companies, ideally of similar nature, agreed close to valuation date. Arguments in the analysis turned on:
  - whether the EDITDA figures for the comparables should be the most recent ones or a weighted average over the three previous years. The Tribunal wanted this on the same basis as the Welcocks figure had been agreed.
  - adjustments for issues outside EDITDA, such as contingent liabilities and debt as well as an earn out clause in one company sale under which targets would have to be met for more value to be paid,
  - the exclusion by the Tribunal of a Community Interest Company with its asset lock making it too different to be comparable.

While giving more weight to comparables nearer the valuation date, so better capturing contemporary conditions in the relevant sector, review of other factors led the Tribunal to find a multiplier of 7.4.

- **profits before taxation** (PBTs) – Welcocks argued that this was relevant basis as it had no debt, putting its capital value at less risk in a way not accounted for in EDITDA analysis. Quoted company accounts were used to support the calculations of Welcocks' enterprise value, based on its operations with regard to funding. The Tribunal, while considering that gearing would see a higher return on equity, found that this approach:
  - showed a market view that being debt-free was an advantage in this sector
  - was to be preferred as more objective than a subjective adjustment for being debt free.

The Tribunal found a multiplier of 11.1 for this approach.

11.9.11 The Tribunal then averaged the three multipliers to give £8.61 million, considering that the uplift given by the inclusion of PBT multiplier:

"fairly reflects the balance between the Claimant's ability to generate good margins from its existing business model and the industry trend towards greater levels of recycling which the Claimant would only have been able to satisfy, in our opinion, by greater capital expenditure in the future."

11.9.12 That was then reduced for:
- income received after the valuation date
- proceeds from the sale of fixed assets
- the release of working capital

but with an addition for professional fees, staff claims and miscellaneous losses.

11.9.13 Other Valuations of Businesses for Compulsory Purchase – Barry Denyer-Green in *Compulsory Purchase and Compensation* (10th Edition) has noted these other cases in which the Tribunal has awarded a value for the business:

Perezic v Bristol Corpn [1955]	No deduction for labour in a one man grocery
Moggridge v Brsitol Corpn [1956]	Value of reduction in profits
Zarraga v Newcastle upon Tyne Corpn [1968]	Wife's wages not deducted; fish and chip shop
Koch v Greater London Council [1969]	Business can have value to owner even if loss-making
Afzal v Rochdale MBC [1980]	Value of corner shop to owner was twice market value
Lindon Print Ltd v West Midlands CC [1987]	Accounts for the preceding year did not show the potential of a printing business
Sceneout Ltd v Central Manchester Development Corpn [1995]	1.77 x profit of laundry with adjustments
Klein v London Underground [1996]	Rejection of shadow losses
Shevlin v Trafford Park DC [1998]	Director's remuneration Depreciation not added back
Aslam v South Bedfordshire DC [1998]	Slaughterhouse; adjustments for income stream risks; 20% discount rate for DCF; 3.81 multiplier
Christa v Highways Agency [2000]	Director's remuneration added back for light engineering firm
Halil v Lambeth LBC [2001]	Wife's earnings not deducted from hairdresser's profits
Matthews v Environment Agency [2003]	Value included value for buildings for catering, shop and amusements
Optical Express (Southern) Ltd v Birmingham City Council [2005]	7.6 x EBITDA
Saglam v Docklands Light Railway [2007]	EDITDA inappropriate for small restaurant, one years' earnings used
Crowley (Contraband Discount Stores) Ltd v Liverpool [2007]	Normalised profit before tax, less tax. Addition of 20% to value for control premium

12. REVIEWING A FARM OR ESTATE BUSINESS

"I keep six honest serving-men
(They taught me all I knew);
Their names are What and Why and When
And How and Where and Who."

(Rudyard Kipling, *Six Honest Serving Men,*
The Elephant's Child)

"The most damaging phrase in the language is 'We've always done it this way'."
Attributed to US Rear Admiral Grace Murray Hopper

12.1   Background

12.1.1 With the expectation that a combination of wider pressures, future policies (indeed possibly also those within the CAP as it develops) and more open markets will prove a driver of much business change, with a need for a focus on financial margin and profit. That seems particularly likely for both England and Wales with proposals to withdraw Basic Payment (with the very high financial margin it offers) entirely with the replacement support offering a lesser margin on what is expected to be lesser payments still requiring action.

12.1.2 With the transitional periods proposed for the policies and the realities of the time needed to understand, manage and deliver change effectively, that is seen to create a time window for doing that by the mid-2020s for those farmers and businesses that wish to manage change rather than accept being buffeted by it.

12.1.3 That conclusion points to the need to start managing that process now, thinking, analysing and understanding the pressures, resources, problems and opportunities and then talking each situation through, reaching decisions about changes and the acting to implement them, so that this can be done successfully in readiness.

12.1.4 An early part of this will be the need to be clear about the objectives of the person, family or business with questions including:
   – why do they have the property?
   – why do they farm?
   – where do they want to be in ten years' time?
   – what is the appetite of the individuals for the challenge?
For some, the business and its profitability, now and in the future, will be paramount. Others may have other objectives, including lifestyle, though few are likely to want to accept unlimited losses. It may simply be an unspoken sense of identity, farming being what they do, or the continuing influence of those now long in the grave.

12.1.5 Equally, there may be conflicting objectives or expectations between the individuals involved as well as asymmetries of information while some may simply not fully understand the position or sometimes wish to do so, with a consequent lack of realism, possibly over what can be drawn from the business. That may call for clarity as conflicts of interest and the identity of the client before that becomes problematic.

12.1.6 Crystallising and securing agreement on such points lays the foundations for the following discussions and decisions.

12.2   Conversations to Come

12.2.1   That points to a major professional role in assisting and supporting families through this, drawing on both the traditional agricultural valuer's skills of observation, assessment, judgement and an understanding of farmers and farms combined with the business appraisal skills sketched in this paper. That role will sometimes be one of managing the discussion of difficult decisions about businesses that may no longer look viable with the result being the farmer, of whatever age, withdrawing wholly or partly from farming. Equally, it will be about exploring new options and businesses as well as negotiating generational change, whether within the family or to/with new people.

12.2.2 The trusted adviser's role will be critical, offering the value of a safe challenger, understanding those involved but giving an external view, helping get things in perspective and drawing on a broader experience. Some clients may need to be talked through the realities of their situation, whether the consequences of making no change or, for those looking positively at change, the practical issues in deciding and making change. It can be a task of helping those who have retreated into busy-ness to summon the appetite to look at their business. That makes it continuing role, assisting the business move from advice and analysis to decision to implementation.

12.2.3   Where substantial business change or non-agricultural **diversification** is in mind that may often be achieved more successfully by an already strong business, not by one that is already failing with management capacity and finances under strain. A poorly judged diversification can risk capital and distract management both possibly better employed in the core business. However, a change in management capacity, as perhaps by generational succession, may offer new opportunities for progress that could not otherwise be made.

12.2.4   With other possible social support and knowledge exchange, it might be useful to encourage the clients to visit others who have already have experience of operating enterprises, ideas or technologies that appear interesting, join a relevant discussion group or find some other way of ensuring a larger perspective and an openness of mind.

12.2.5   It is worth understanding the circumstances that have made success possible, from location to specialist skill, or capital from the sale of development land. Where possible, it can be still more informative still to look at failures, with the problems and the lessons to be learnt from difficulties found with a project.

12.2.6   Specialist professional help by the valuer or others may be needed on technical issues but the larger need looks to be for sustained, rounded appraisal, strategic advice and support with facilitation to helping the conversation move forward within the family and others with special support and knowledge exchange.

12.2.7   Finally, decisions, once reached, will need to be implemented, again likely to require professional support. Little of the analysis, benchmarking or advice will be of more than curiosity value if it does not lead to considered decisions that are then followed through.

12.2.8   With that background, this chapter considers how to approach the underlying business review and the exploration of options.

12.3 The Factors of Production

12.3.1 A business can be looked at as the use of four factors of production to produce value. These are:

- *management*, the skills to deliver the business and typically about both strategic direction and attention to detail achieving continuing marginal improvement across all parts of the business being as fundamental as any more radical change
- *land*, for a farm the land and buildings used in the business, whether owned, rented or with access by other means, and with its potential, constraints and location
- *capital*, the use of money, whether internally funded, borrowed or raised externally and including the ability of the business to borrow as collateral is measure of the potential reach of the business where its use is justified
- *labour*, the operational work of people, whether the business owners, employed staff or from contractors.

One approach to reviewing a business is to consider the best use, both short and long term, of each of these and how they may be best improved to deliver more value.

12.3.2 While working in that way from the factors of production fits well with classic farm management approaches and is most directly geared to production economics, it can be developed to consider:

- other uses of farm resources, from building conversions to forestry or renewable energy
- to consider other resources altogether, including the opportunities of environmental issues, whether through official schemes or private sector initiatives, as well as the challenges posed by environmental change and regulation.

12.4 Environmental Options

12.4.1 The growing discussion of climate change and other environmental issues has seen more use of the language of natural capital and ecosystem services as well as greater discussion of sustainability and resilience.

12.4.2 "Natural capital" uses the analogy of a balance sheet to express the environment as a stock of natural assets which can be increased or run down. Common examples of subjects often considered as natural capital include:

- biodiversity
- soils
- land
- stocks of carbon
- good quality water and air
- landscape
- accessible nature.

12.4.3 Ecosystem services, not always entirely distinct in practical discussion from natural capital, include such subjects as:

- crops, livestock and timber
- climate change mitigation
- improved water quality and supply
- improved soil quality
- improved air quality
- pollination
- energy supply
- services to human, animal and plant health and wellbeing.

12.4.4 Some of these already play a greater or lesser part in productive markets, as for food. Others are more often taken for granted by markets which impose costs on society that are not charged for or recognised in product prices. We are now seeing some of these becoming a concern of government and business, stimulating new income flows and potential economic opportunities, whether from agri-environment schemes, the concerns of water companies, the pressure on large corporations from the Taskforce on Climate-related Disclosure or developers seeking bio-diversity offsetting.

12.4.5 As one example, the stock of carbon stored away from the atmosphere can be understood as natural capital. That stock of carbon (natural capital) is depleted where peat erodes or soil management releases carbon into the atmosphere. Improving the soil's organic matter will offer an ecosystem service and add to this form of natural capital. It may also offer such other services as aiding water quality as well as assisting productive agriculture with crop resilience and other benefits.

12.4.6 Another example would be the recognition that a greater number and variety of invertebrates will support much of the rest of animal diversity and aid pollination of crops as a service.

12.4.7 Farms and estates typically have the ability to respond to these new demands in ways that may range:
- from supporting existing incomes, as by improving many soils with more organic matter
- to finding a more profitable use of less productive land.
In short, the environment can be seen to be developing to offer a potential as a business enterprise that can offer profit from land management by providing these services to those that need or want to pay for them.

12.4.8 Recognising environmental challenges may be equally material, whether physical ones such as greater exposure to flooding or new pests, or regulatory pressure from measures to reduce ammonia emissions to limiting the tools for crop management.

12.4.9 Further, as the general and broad concept of "natural capital" can, in practice, be seen to be close to the traditional rural concept of stewardship, considering these issues can fit with protecting the long-term value of the business and its assets.

12.4.10 That points to the potential in considering what a business may be able to offer as these new demands and markets develop.

12.4.11 The assessment and appraisal of natural capital assets includes the identification of:
- what those natural capital assets are, and
- their importance.
That might include the maintenance of a landscape, the sequestration of carbon or identifying biodiversity assets such as habitats or species diversity that underpin the ability of the property to deliver ecosystem services.

12.4.12 That might consider both:
- their value on the property itself, where they may already offer a value to the existing user. That might be case with timber or soil improvement, both directly adding benefit to the property
- their value more widely to others and society. This may be much greater as with the value of soil improvement sequestering carbon as well as aiding farming. A natural capital asset might only be seen as being beneficial in the wider context and landscape.

12.5 Sustainability and Resilience

12.5.1 Both the financial and the environmental issues can be subsumed in the larger concepts of the sustainability and resilience of the business. For farming and land management these appear similar to the traditional idea of stewardship, leaving the property for the next generation in better condition than it was inherited. They fit with the longstanding injunction to "farm as though you'll live forever".

12.5.2 In its broadest terms, sustainability is usually seen as being able to meet the needs of current generations without compromising the ability of future generations to meet their own needs

12.5.3 Resilience is not only the ability to withstand shocks, of any sort, but to recover from them, "to bounce back better".

12.5.4 In practice, this might be best seen for the business as about building resources, including:
- personal skills, from training to outlook
- the efficiency of the business in its use of resources (productivity)
- financial resources, assets including the ability to borrow but to undue exposure to debt
- the quality of the farming assets, from the soils to the genetics of livestock
- the management of farming such as the use and protection of nutrients
- resilience against shocks from financial pressure to flooding
- the ability to use technology and innovate to meet changing requirements and markets
- developing the business to serve markets to achieve improved margins.

12.5.5 There are then larger expectations about matters such as:
- climate change mitigation with the sequestration of carbon
- climate change adaptation as say managing water flow
- energy efficiency
- water and air quality
- biodiversity and
- waste management.

Pressures to improve these are likely to come from public expectations, government schemes, regulations and taxation as well as the requirements or opportunities driven by the supply chain and other private sector initiatives.

12.5.6 The pressures requiring this approach will not only be economic but, for some, those of repeated flooding and, for most, the stress for farming from periodic drought and heat stress as well as new pests and diseases. A resilient approach will then also seek out the opportunities in this and the adaptations required to take them.

12.6 Information Gathering and Preliminary Review

12.6.1 Without good information the whole process of a review will be weakened. The agricultural valuer may already know much about a client's business, its structure and operations from work over the years but this is unlikely to be comprehensive and there can always be changes or surprises.

12.6.2 The last three years' accounts will offer a starting point, supplemented by financial projections based on there being no change in the business with accompanying balance sheets and cash flows. In combination, they will set out the foundations for this work.

12.6.3 This calls for identifying:
- who are all the characters in play?
  - what are their skills and weaknesses:
    - in management?
    - in current enterprises?
    - in developing new ones?
  - what are their resources?
  - what are their attitudes to risk and enterprise?
  - prospects and plans for generational change with risks of death and divorce
  - how vulnerable is the business to losing any of them?
  - how are they housed?
  - who has control of the business and the property, both legal and practical?
- what property do they own and rent?
  - who are the owners and tenants of each part?
  - if tenanted, how secure is that occupation?
- what is the business?
  - what are the enterprises?
  - how is it structured
  - who plays what parts in the business?
  - are there issues about supply chains, marketing or customers?
- are the premises, buildings and equipment fit for purpose?
  - do the facilities meet legal standards?
  - do they need improvement?
  - are they surplus and available for other uses?
  - what capital investment is needed? can it be financed?
- how is the business performing physically?
  - key indicators for performance of the enterprises conducted
  - yields – are there yield maps for cropping?
  - soil surveys
- how is the business performing financially?
  - review the accounts for several recent years
  - how sensitive are they to changes in price and performance?
  - what are the levels of drawings?
  - what is the debt position?
  - how much could it sensibly borrow?
  - can it stand a sudden call for capital?
  - could it stand an increase in interest rates?
  - what potential risks/liabilities are foreseen in the near future?
  - are there taxation issues?
- look ahead a decade – what might be the position then?

12.6.4 That can be considered as a part of an initial review of strengths, weaknesses, opportunities and threats.

12.6.5 It may often highlight issues of succession planning, typically a matter concerning people, land, business, housing, finance and expectations.

12.6.6 Where the business involves several members of a family, this review could, as it proceeds, lead to discussion of a documents, perhaps such as a "family charter", developing in draft, setting out:
- objectives, business and personal
- attitudes handling the business and assets through succession and death

- identifying roles, responsibilities and rewards (some of these may already covered in a partnership, company or trust document)

and so aiding the conversation.

12.7 Look at Cashflow

12.7.1 The immediate prospects for the business turn on its liquidity: its cash holdings and its ability to generate cash to meet its liabilities as well reward its principals.

12.7.2 Prepare a monthly cash flow for the next twelve months and so beginning to look at whether the business is generating money and, if so, from what, where it is weak and whether it is meeting drawings. Testing the thinking of the business and its position, this begins to expose the dynamics of the business with the range from inadequate cash generation to unsustainable drawings.

12.7.3 That cash flow can then be tested for sensitivity to varying yields and prices, building up a picture of the business as its stands and testing vulnerability. While market volatility is an issue, sustained low prices and poor margins are worse.

12.7.4 That review paves the way to setting targets for:
- profit – encouraging the focus on margin
- physical performance – yields, etc.
- cash generation and management.

12.8 Looking Ahead

12.8.1 With the prospect of significant changes in support and markets over the coming few years:
- roll that cashflow forward over the next three or five years
- see how it interacts with the accounts
- take out of issues foreseen from the information gathering stage
- again, consider how changes in prices and yields might affect it.

Then adjust for the reduction/withdrawal of BPS (especially in England and Wales).

12.8.2 Describe and analyse the resulting picture, judging what, if any, lifestyle the present business would fund over that period for those who will be depending on it.

12.9 Beginning the Change and Considering Options

12.9.1 For some businesses the review may now have reached a sobering point, one of which they may have long been tacitly aware but avoiding. However, that appraisal is then the basis for deciding how to act to improve the outcome.

12.9.2 It is important that the review considers all possible options, no matter how apparently unpalatable some may seem. While some members of a farming family may be intrinsically opposed to withdrawing from a business or from the farm, those businesses that are facing serious challenge need an effective review that considers those options.

12.9.3 In broad terms, most farming businesses have four strategic options:
(a) maintaining the status quo
(b) restructuring the existing business, its operations and assets
(c) leaving or reducing the business but retaining all or the bulk of the property
(d) leaving or reducing the business and disposing of some or all of the property.

In most cases, the discussion might usually centre on option (b). In practice, by having reached this point it may be that option (a) is no longer a tenable option and it may take effort to consider option (c).

12.9.4   While option (d) could be an anathema to many farming clients, where public sector, third sector or institutional estates are under review low rates of return may make progressive or outright disposal a much more attractive prospect, outweighing the sentiment that may bulk larger for farming or estate owning families.

12.9.5   Returning to family farming and similar businesses, these alternative strategies may encompass many options, both more "tactical" and more "strategic".

12.9.6   Perhaps at the strategic end is the tension between:
- being a commodity producer and so, likely to be a price taker, with a focus on controlling unit costs of production
- looking for ways to be more sheltered from commodity competition with options from:
  ○ producing or marketing produce that secures a higher margin (so adding value, processing finding a niche, differentiating the product, doing something special or different)
  ○ to adding other income, whether off farm employment or developing assets or businesses based on the farm.

12.9.7   More specifically these can perhaps be loosely grouped into this non-exhaustive list of approaches and possible points for consideration:
- running the existing business more efficiently
  ○ looking for improved operations throughout the business
  ○ improving timeliness
  ○ soil surveys and improved management
  ○ arrangements for sharing machinery and labour
  ○ more generally, working with neighbours
  ○ use of contractors with better machinery
  ○ joining a buying group
  ○ taking advantage of technology in the field and in the office
  ○ reviewing marketing
  ○ reviewing loan costs
- the consideration of the application of innovation in technology for production, management and marketing
  ○ use of data
  ○ using new machinery
- what use might be made of future productivity support (with its possible obligations)
  ○ grants/loans
  ○ knowledge exchange
  ○ additional skills and training
- reducing exposure, activity and costs, perhaps in combination with taking other work or reducing lifestyle
- changing the farming enterprises adopted or the ways in which they are delivered
  ○ contracting out operations, such as heifer rearing (or becoming the heifer rearer for others)
  ○ specialising further
  ○ reviewing more radical changes on marginal arable ground, for example alternate year cropping and perhaps using the land released for public goods schemes or others to graze

- o considering organic or other categories to reposition the business
- o bringing in another farming enterprise if there are the skills, capital and management to do so
- o finding a farming system that allows the farmer to take a job off the farm
- where viable markets might be now and in the future
- developing the business
  - o adding value to produce
  - o developing processing
  - o seeking higher margin markets
  - o developing brands
  - o are grants, with their obligations, worth taking?
- diversifying into a non-agricultural business
  - o define the project and test it
  - o is there the management capacity?
  - o what other skills are needed?
  - o why has it not been done before by the business?
  - o is the business financially strong enough to do this with its risks?
  - o consider the position if its development over-runs on both budget and time
  - o does it fit with the farming business or compete with it for resources?
- exploiting the location of the business
- reviewing the land base
  - o does all present land contribute to the business?
  - o how might a reduced acreage fit with overheads?
  - o where expansion is necessary, is it feasible?
- what might be the opportunities to take good advantage of environmental possibilities so that, with all their obligations, they contribute to financial margin?
  - o using existing schemes
  - o looking at the emerging outlines of future schemes (such as ELMS in England, Sustainable Farming in Wales)
  - o opportunities from the private sector, including bio-diversity offsetting
  - o using yield mapping and soil surveys to help judge which land might be more profitable in options that are less focussed on production
  - o where might environmental options aid production (such as improving soil organic matter)
  - o is there a case for more trees, woodland or forestry whether as:
    - an enterprise (biomass production)
    - complementing farming (as on poorer land, shelter belts, sheltering stock) or
    - in place of less productive farming (as for value, amenity, grant aid, …)
    - the setting for other business on the farm?
- making the best use of assets
  - o letting assets out
  - o renewable energy
  - o potential for building development in the coming decade?
  - o non-agricultural diversification potential
  - o how long might development take and at what cost?

12.9.8 As that array of options and questions shows, the outcome across the farming and rural economy is likely to be much more varied, potentially with less reliance overall on commodity production, calling for a greater range of skills and posing a wider range of risks. However, none of that is necessarily new though the pressures for this shift may become stronger.

12.10 Reviewing the People Involved

12.10.1 The business is a function of the people involved, each with their own position, disposition, appetites, issues, abilities, limitations, histories and concerns. They may be 40 and not really interested in a farming business that they were expected to take on or 70 and energetic about innovation. Limitations or ability, health or finance may be a factor. There may be:
- a proficient child, child-in-law, grandchild or other family member ready and able to succeed
- an employee, relative, neighbour or new entrant who might farm the land well, or
- no one to take it in its current structure.

12.10.2 Questions to explore might include:
- who has the skills and energy to make the best of this?
- does this fit with succession plans within the family?
- do others have better skills and capital?
- does this lead to arrangements with other farmers?
- does this lead to letting some or all of the land out?

12.10.3 Beneath those questions is a consideration of willingness and appetite and attitudes to risk and change in both the current and any future generation.

12.10.4 The review process outlined here may lead to the existing business being affirmed, finding ways to improve it and adapt with opportunities and circumstances. Equally, it may point to fundamental changes that should perhaps have already been considered and which have been avoided by receipt of Basic Payment.

12.10.5 Where larger scale changes are suggested they are likely to involve hard decisions and often hard work as well as advice. The answers will be individual to each set of circumstances and people: that a decisions is radical does not make it right while settling on little or no change may be to miss the chance for the business and the family.

12.10.6 Changing and developing the business may call on the skills and experience of other members of the family than the presumed farming successor. For example, where marketing and public communications or project management might be needed it might well be that others have more skills. Using them may then mean less distraction from the management needed to continue and improve the farming business.

12.10.7 The farm may change its shape and size if land is bought or sold, or tenancies sought or relinquished.

12.10.8 If developing the business, they could need the commitment, borrowing or raising of further capital with the time and management to deliver success from that.

12.10.9 Engaging in greater co-operation with others, whether in pooling machinery and labour, sharing operations or through other means, would require a willingness to co-operate and acting some cost in loss of independence if this is to give effective results.

Even with a willingness to co-operate, something will still turn on the chemistry between those involved. Fundamentally, these turn on shared understanding and trust but that may enable cover for holidays and sickness and the larger benefits of shared discussions. Where this leads to a combined operation, it might need its own office, rather than appearing to be based on one party's business.

12.10.10 It may be that it is time for the present head of business, of whatever age, to withdraw, in favour of those who might meet the challenge better with skills, attitudes, capital/collateral and confidence in handling innovation in both technology and markets. That might be by:

- family succession, whether to children, grandchildren or other relatives
- using contractors, releasing working capital and the immediate work but perhaps retaining status
- working with neighbours as where efficiencies can be gained by pooling machinery or combining operations
- letting the land out, releasing working capital
- sale of the farm or surrender of tenancies.

As well as reviewing the potential for using Entrepreneurs' Relief from Capital Gains Tax on any disposals of assets, that may require consideration of future income and housing and understanding whether they are genuine limitations or excuses for inertia.

12.11   Succession

12.11.1 Farming is a sector overwhelmingly comprising family businesses; some 30 per cent of farm businesses are said to have continuity from before 1900. That means that the passage of time drives the question of succession though it may be precipitated by death or serious illness. In analytical terms, it can be seen as one way of posing the issue of the exit strategy for the current owner, here generally involving passing the business to someone in the family. This a key part of considering how both family and the farming business might respond to the economic pressures outlined in the Introduction.

12.11.2 More narrowly, there is the potential for statutory succession to a tenancy protected by the Agricultural Holdings Act 1986 or the Agricultural Holdings (Scotland) Act 1991, each of which define the classes of potentially eligible successors, the qualifications required of them, the procedures to be followed and the dispute resolution mechanisms. Forward planning within the tenant's family can often provide answers to any difficulties that might found in this but if they are foreseen to be unsurmountable then that will also frame expectations and approaches

12.11.3 In farming, succession concerns both the conduct of farming as a business and the ownership of the assets. Where there is a prospective successor interesting in and competent at farming, then there is often a long transition, first moving from working on the farm to taking a growing role in management, perhaps from a specific aspect or enterprise to increasing involvement in the broader business and financial matters. Ownership of assets typically passes last in that process.

12.11.4 Sometimes, the succession to the business (but much more rarely the assets) may consciously involve a member of staff, perhaps by establishing a joint venture with a longstanding and skilled employee as the means to continue a business that also serves to manage the land.

12.11.5 Where no family member is actively interested in taking on the operational farming, the approaches can range from:
- recognising that there will be no succession but simply considering the handling of the assets, with the questions being about whether and how the present farmer might manage retirement

to

- developing a structure whereby interested family members can remain involved in ownership or strategy of the continuing business while having others manage it.

Options for the latter include:
- retaining the land and letting it on a tenancy
- other forms of joint venture
- taking on a farm manager and so with working capital and risk still involved in the business
- moving to a company structure with individual family interests converted into shareholdings with management accountable to shareholders

Working though this will see answers vary with the individuals involved and also with the scale and the enterprise pursued, whether considering a small livestock farm where all work is done the aging owner or a large farm with specialist operations where the farmer's activity is more likely to be management.

12.11.6 Increased longevity can make it important for farming families to consider the question of exit, retirement and succession as it can be easy to let these drift, confusing expectations and potential accumulating frustrations to the detriment of the business, especially where the effectiveness of the current management may weaken.

12.11.7 This requires identifying the potential successor(s), reconciling any competing family interests. With the skills, outlook and energy likely to be required, that could mean being prepared to jump a generation.

12.11.8 Equally, succession should not be imposed as an obligation on the next or any generation. There will be points when it right for the family to take a different direction, including withdrawing fully or partly from farming but seeking to do so in the spirit of making a positive change to new life.

12.11.9 Succession has to be prepared for by the successor, acquiring the skills and experience to respond to the challenges to be faced in the coming generation. That will typically involve formal training, the benefit of the perspective given by experience away from the farm and an openness to continuing improvement. Where there are competing calls on family assets, the future financing of the business needs to be considered.

12.11.10 Those factors point to succession as an evolving process, requiring discussion and management, potentially with the development of a framework or plan. This process may often be assisted by an outside adviser to help the parties in general appraisal and strategy and on particular points and problems. An external perspective can help where something has been overlooked or has become an unnecessary or disproportionately large obstacle. An external trusted adviser can also help crystallise decisions which can then be implemented.

12.11.11 Classically, the factors which impede succession, whether in reality or as excuses, include:
- farming being so integral to the identity of the farmer that formal retirement is not attractive, in which case scaling back activity may be part of the answer

- living too close to the business to notice the changes brought by time
- a reluctance to broach issues (sometimes because of previous issues in the family over succession)
- concern about fairness between the farming and non-farming members of the family
- lack of resources for retirement income, sometimes a version of the question about how many people a farm can support
- housing.

12.12   Housing

12.12.1   For some owner occupiers the challenge can be to manage housing while keeping the farming property; more tenants may not have the resources. If the farmer wishes to retire in the house he has always lived in, then the housing issue is for the new farmer whether from within or outside the family. Equally, the farmer may wish or need to retire away from the farm, whether to adapted accommodation or for a change.

12.12.2   However, there are opportunities. While the lesser development pressure in much of Scotland and Northern Ireland may often help them be more practical in recognising such situations:
- in England, paragraph 79 of the National Planning Policy Framework has since July 2018 accepted the potential case for isolated housing where it is for someone taking majority control of a farming business (an argument that seems adaptable to someone ceding control of such a business)
- again in England, Class Q offers the opportunity to a farm to convert agricultural buildings, old or modern, into up to five dwellings, using constrained permitted development rights and so not requiring planning permission. While conversion can be more expensive than a new building, some 300 such dwellings are created each year while it seems that inn many more cases it enables a useful planning permission to be obtained. At the time of writing, Scotland is considering a possible similar policy.
- in Wales, the TAN 6 policy has since 2011 sets tests that can enabled farmers to seek a second dwelling to enable a transfer of business control. The great majority of applications are approved.

12.12.3   There may be opportunities for negotiation that unlock the required value between landlord and tenant as well as within families. Bodies such as the Addington Fund and some housing associations such as Hastoe might also be able to enable answers. It may yet be that the post-Brexit de-linking of residual Basic Payment and its possible availability as a lump sum in England might ease some such discussions.

12.12.4   These issues are explored more fully in *Retirement Housing for Farmers in the United Kingdom: A Review of the Issues, Experiences and Possible Answers* (https://www.caav.org.uk/docs/Retirement%20Housing%20for%20Farmers%20in%20the%20UK.pdf).

13. FACILITATING DISCUSSION – HELPING PEOPLE FIND THE ANSWERS

13.1   Introduction

13.1.1   As outlined, this process of business review and planning calls on the broader use of personal and empathetic skills to help clients, such as a farming or landowning family (or members of one), finding and developing their own answers to the situation that they are in. According to the circumstances and personal skills, this might be handled by the agricultural valuer or by calling in someone independent and skilled as a facilitator.

13.1.2   In this chapter, "facilitator" is used for both roles but in the capacity of facilitating a solution, rather than as giving professional advice. This is specifically about understanding those involved as individuals and considering the relationships between them. The boundary between this role and professional work may in reality be quite blurred, calling for some clarity about instructions and accountability and looking ahead for potential conflicts of interest.

13.1.3   Such a process of facilitating discussion does not need there to be a dispute or even a difference to be resolved but can, for a family wanting to look ahead, directly enable the issues here to be opened, explored and tested for ways forward to be found. This may concern topics such as business policy, generational succession or a partnership dissolution – all possibly difficult for those involved to tackle but where an outside neutral person with the right skills can open and sustain a confidential conversation in ways the parties could not but can then be helped to sustain.

13.1.4   At the lowest key level, it could be viewed as enabling a private conversation that might not otherwise happen (or be done well) without the facilitator, answering situations where three may be company but two a crowd.

13.1.5   However this may be done, the facilitator should manage the process so that all involved have their say, contributing to the outcome. The process requires respect for each party.

13.2   A Possible Structure of Issues for Review

13.2.1   While each situation will be different, there may be some themes that will be found and need to be tackled in many cases, though the emphasis between them will vary and other will be met.

13.2.2   These can include:
- understand the history of the situation with the influence of previous generations and past events, how they were tackled and what lessons were taken from them
- what each of those now and prospectively involved might want for the business and their lives
- patterns of communication and non-communication in the family and with other key individuals, including the dynamics of who might be able to work well with each other in the future
- a shared understanding of what assets are involved, from land and machinery to houses and pensions, and what they are worth and also of the liabilities and debts
- looking ahead to where family members might be or want to be in ten years time
- looking at expectations of what work might be required, its conditions and what might be its reward
- how housing is to be managed
- conclusions, decisions and a framework for implementation.

13.3 Acting as a Facilitator

13.3.1 Where the root of resolving the issues lie in the characters of the people involved, the personal skills for this work are such that someone brought in as a facilitator does not need to have relevant technical or professional knowledge but the ability to help clients find their way forward to the point where professional skills may then be needed to deliver and implement the outcome. Some have specific skills in conflict resolution. Equally though, knowing the range of technical issues and possibilities may aid the optimal outcome.

13.3.2 The fundamental requirement is that the facilitator gains and maintains the trust of the parties so that they will accept the facilitator's encouragement of a process that is open to all of those involved in seeking a way forward. Any appearance of bias or conflict of interest has to be avoided. When considering expressing a view, care should be taken in this lest it compromise that neutrality. While the benefits of a valuer's professional knowledge and instincts should assist in identifying a way forward, it can prejudice matters if the facilitator is (or is seen to be) too committed to any one solution – it has to be the family's answer.

13.3.3 Other making for a good facilitator include objectivity, empathy, intuition, pragmatism, realism, an ability to help people think afresh and being a good communicator within a small group.

13.3.4 In essence, these qualities are about being interested in people, their problems and potential solutions and being skilful in that interest with an ability to engender trust so that even reserved parties will open up and play their part in the facilitation process.

13.4 Moving to a Facilitator From Outside the Business

Where a family, a business or other group accepts the involvement of a facilitator that is the first step on the road. That requires:
- proposing the idea successfully within the family or business where it may be there is a long history of avoiding strategic conversations
- finding one who will be appropriate (the CAAV may be able to assist with that).

13.5 Approaching the Discussion

13.5.1 All relevant parties need to be involved and progressively drawn into the process as it develops with their participation. That point to two particular issues:
- ensuring that all significant personalities are present and involved
- maintaining a sense of process so that progress achieved is secured and can be built on.

The process is vulnerable to the risk that something that appears agreed falls apart as one of more parties reconsider a position, view or opinion, perhaps after discussing it with someone not there, whether spouse, partner, adviser or other. Especially where the facilitation concerns a family, as so often for farming, those people can play a key role in either supporting a family plan or jeopardising it. That makes it preferable to have evidently key personalities involved but that is not always acceptable to other family members or the other parties prefer to keep a distance.

13.5.2 Once in place, the facilitator needs to understand the positions, interests and needs of the parties:
- where, among the parties, does the power, financial or emotional, lie?
- what are dynamics between the individuals? The answer is likely to involve both family history and family expectations and may even be changed by the

presence of the facilitator. In a farming family, the place of non-farming members can be further factor as may be the influence of previous generations, whether dead or absent.

- even if they do not know it consciously themselves, what might they want?
- what agendas, motives, concerns or interests are hidden?
- how might each party play the facilitation process, with the range of possibilities from skilled and effective communicators to those who cannot explain themselves or even are terrified of the process.
- who is used to being over-ruled but needs the chance to speak for this process to be complete?
- who is abdicating responsibility?
- what is being said by someone's silence?
- how can the parties come to see the situation from someone else's perspective? If there are problems, they are likely to have been there for some time with varying levels of aggravation, avoidance or intractability.

13.6   The Opening Meeting for a Family Conversation

13.6.1   Where it is recognised that there is to be a specific process for the family, rather than long standing discussions continuing to evolve, that process will typically start with a collective meeting of the parties with the facilitator. This can be crucial to achieving the final agreement with the facilitator enabling each person to talk about the situation, perhaps the opportunity to say things not said before.

13.6.2   The room needs to be able to accommodate all parties comfortably and in a way that gives all an equal place at the table – a circular or diamond, rather than a rectangular, table may assist as no one will then be at the head of it. It may be that it is harder to disagree with someone who is not sitting across the table.

13.6.3   The facilitator should be concerned that all have their say. Silent, junior or less involved members of a family may feel overshadowed by those who are vocal, senior or currently active in managing the business. Siblings not involved in the farm may feel that their role is awkward or disadvantaged as also may daughters/sons-in-law. Sometimes the facilitator might first ask those furthest from the core of the business to outline their thoughts and expectations, working towards the dominant party.

13.6.4   Where there are deeper issues, the process might see some expression of emotion for which the meeting provides a controlled environment.

13.6.5   As the process develops so further meetings may be held. It can take time for people to absorb and work through points, adjusting their reactions. As objectives come to be found and positions reshaped, so these may be more about means of implementation, where professional advisers will often be important.

13.6.6   Professional Advisers? – The presence of one or more other professional advisers may also affect the dynamics of the meeting; that presence could act to help or hinder the process.

13.6.7   There can be complicated relationships with and between advisers or the parties involved which may make the facilitation or discussion more difficult (or change its character), such as:

- the possible emphasis on specific technical concerns (such as tax) with potentially binary answers rather than on achieving a holistic, workable and sustainable plan for the future

- the "family solicitor" often, in reality, being the solicitor to the head of the family, rather than for the family as a whole
- a key party hiding behind an adviser or alternatively being reluctant to challenge one
- it sometimes being difficult for one adviser to question the advice of another, as say, a valuer querying the tax advice of the accountant but unwilling to give competing advice
- not all advisers being present, for reasons that might include the cost for a process that is not guaranteed to reach a conclusion
- parties not wanting all advisers to know all aspects of the matter when professional advice turns on the information given or the questions asked.

13.6.8 A particular adviser may thus give confidence to one or more of those involved but equally may bring their own agenda, perhaps especially if there for one of the parties only, where two professionals face each other in the meeting or suspect that the process is likely to lead to future disagreements rather than a solution. At this stage, the facilitation process may be better seen as one of psychological evolution with the professional implementation following, provided that any solution found is feasible.

13.6.9 Yet an outcome that cannot be implemented or involves major technical problems may be worse than no outcome, with the parties set back by finding their hard won agreement frustrated by realities that may prove to favour one party. The answer may be for the initial record of the outcome to focus on objectives and intentions with implementation as the next stage.

13.6.10 Ultimately, it is the parties who have to take responsibility for the process – without this it is always going to be fruitless. Those coming to facilitation without commitment to the process can cause it to fail, however good the facilitator.

13.7   The Facilitator's Roles
13.7.1   The facilitator's role is just that – to facilitate a solution, doing so in a way that offers the greatest chance of binding all parties into it. That means working with the parties so that the individuals come to move forward in a way that they developed and agreed.

13.7.2   Where the facilitator does intervene that becomes a new fact in the dynamics of the meeting, one that cannot be retracted.

13.7.3   The facilitator is gathering information, only having seen what the parties have provided as briefing and aware that here will be evidence or argument that has not been mentioned. Tackling this will require:
- assessing body language
- watching the parties interact with each other
- considering whether someone is saying what they believe they are expected to say, what they think others want to hear or (deliberately or not) reshaping memories and explanations
- being alert for the fleeting emergence of a salient issue
- considering the possible motives behind statements, questions or other actions.

13.7.4   That requires the techniques of "active listening", understanding and taking forward what has been said with the facilitator:
- repeating an interesting word, phrase or idea back to the person who put it so they can hear and assess their own words ("reflecting")

- rephrasing something that has been said to sum it up and help clarify its meaning
- summarising, again to check understanding and offer clarification
- checking the impact positions, decisions or results might have to ensure a realistic view ("reality checking").

13.7.5   Those processes may make it right for the facilitator on occasion to put a conflicting view to a party, acting as a devil's advocate, to prompt reaction, increase understanding or draw out underlying concerns.

13.7.6   It may be that the facilitator has at some point been given information in confidence by one of the parties – that confidence must be respected.

13.7.7   As the discussions develop so the facilitator will encourage progress, often with an approach based on achieving future outcomes, rather than just the present position. Where an impasse appears, the discussion may need to be taken round it or a new approach sought. That may require "parking" a point that has become difficult while others are taken forward. Where a party is obstructive, the facilitator may ask for the reason or problem to be articulated.

13.7.8   As possible solutions or offers emerge, they have to be understood with an assessment of what they involve and how far they are robust answers.

13.7.9   While much of the progress may be more psychological than formal, with positions and outlooks reshaped and logjams broken, points or objectives that are agreed should be recorded as a conclusion or to bank gains made for succeeding meetings.

13.7.10 At the end of a facilitation meeting, the facilitator might ask the parties to say what their joint (and sometimes individual) objectives are, making a note which is then read back to them to ensure that they all agree with the wording and, more importantly, its meaning. That can then be recorded as a "charter" or "plan" with copies held by all.

13.8   The Outcome and Thereafter

13.8.1   As conclusions and a solution do emerge so the means to take them forward for implementation should be put in place. Professional advisers may be very important to this being done effectively with the instructions framed by the outcome of the facilitation.

13.8.2   The primary objective of a facilitation is usually the production of a "workable and sustainable" plan specific to the parties (say, a family) and their situation. That plan, when achieved, should contain the agreed objectives and tasks to be achieved, stating the specific responsibilities for individuals and time frames for actions by them, to avoid them being "someone else's responsibility".)

13.8.3   Before agreeing on an allocation of tasks and responsibilities between the parties it should be established that those being asked do have the capability, skill and commitment to complete the task. The facilitator needs to be wary of overburdening individuals who come forward but may not be able to deliver, whether by lack of authority, ability or other reasons. Those reasons might include a possible lack of commitment, returning to the core task of engaging the parties in the process, fundamental to a good outcome.

13.8.4   Where major decisions and plans have been agreed at a key meeting, it can be important to fix the date for a follow-up meeting to maintain a sense of common process and so progress

13.8.5   The outcome may often need to be a "living" plan that will be regularly reviewed (say, annually) so that it keeps the parties moving forward as situations change. The plan needs to be flexible enough to adapt and evolve with changing circumstances, objectives and desires. In some cases, the facilitator will (where appropriate) make contact to monitor progress.

APPENDIX

SCHEDULE OF CASES

A v A [2004] EWHC 2818

Afzal v Rochdale MBC [1980] 1 EGLR 157

AR v AR (Treatment of Inherited Wealth) [2011] EWHC 2717

B v B (Financial Provision) [1990] 1 FLR 20

Bede Distributors Ltd v Newcastle upon Tyne Corporation [1973] 26 P&CR 298

Burdon v Barkus [1862] 4 De GF&J 42

Cash and Carry v Inspector of Taxes [1998] STC (SCD) 46

Caton's Administrators v Couch (Inspector of Taxes) [1995] (STC (SCD) 34

Charkham v IRC [1997] LT DET/3-6/1995

Charman v Charman [2006] 2 FLR 422

CR v CR [2007] EWHC 3206 (Fam)

D v D and B Limited [2007] EWHC] 278 (Fam)

Davies v H&R Ecroyd Ltd [1996] 30 EG 97

Dawe v Dawe [1976] Fam Law 51

Evans v Evans [1990] 1 FLR 319

Faulks v Faulks [1992] 15 EG 92

Fisher Meredith v JH [2012] EWHC 408 (Fam)

G Pratt and Sons v HMRC [2011] UKFTT 416 (TC)

Gilbert v Revenue and Customs [2011] UKFTT 705 (TC)

Goldstein v Levy Gee [2003] EWHC 1574

Ham v Bell [2016] EWHC 1791

Ham v Ham [2013] EWCA Civ 1301

IRC v Muller and Co's Margarine Ltd [1901] AC 217

Lurcot v Wakely [1911-13] All ER Rep 41

McArthur v Revenue and Customs [2008] UKSPC 700

Miller v Miller [2006] UKHL 24

Moorish v Moorish [1984] Fam Law 26

N v N (Financial Provision: Sale of Company) [2001] 2 FLR 69

P v P (Financial Provision: Lump Sum) [1978] 1 WLR 483

P v P Inherited Property [2004] EWHC 1364 (Fam).

Pastoral Finance Association Ltd v The Minister [1914] AC 1083

Popat v Schonchhatra [1997] EWCA [1997] Civ 1966

R v R (Lump Sum Repayments) [2003] EWHC 3197 (Fam)

Radmacher v Granatino [2010] UKSC 42; [2008] EWCA Civ 1304

Re Lynall [1968] 47 TC 375

Reynolds v Manchester City Council [1981] 257 EG 939

Ryde International plc v London Regional Transport (No 2) [2004] 2 EGLR 1

TL v ML [2006] 1 FLR 263.

Wakerley v St Edmundsbury Borough Council [1977] 249 EG 639

Watson v Secretary of State for Air [1954] 3 All ER 582

Welcocks Skips Limited v Network Rail Infrastructure Limited [2019] UKUT 162 (LC)

Welford v EDF Energy Networks Ltd [2007] 2 EGLR 1

White v White [2001] 1 AC 596

Wild v Wild [2018] EWHC 2197

Wimpey & Co v Middlesex County Council [1938] 3 All ER 781

CAAV numbered publications

Mediation for Agricultural Valuers (No. 235)	£100
Good Practice in Statutory Compensation Claims (No. 234)	£100
Building Reinstatement Cost Assessments for Farms and Estates (No. 231)	£75
Guide to the Amnesty for Tenant's Improvements in Scotland (No. 229)	£35
The Letting and Management of Residential Property in Wales 2017 (No. 228)	£100
Taxation of Rural Dwellings (No. 227)	£100
Tenancies, Conacre and Licences: Arrangements for Occupying Agricultural Land in Northern Ireland (2015) (No. 225)	£75
A Review of Tenant Right Valuation (2015) (No. 224)	£75
Means of Dispute Resolution (2015) (No. 223)	£75
2015 Update on Residential Tenancy Regulations In England, Wales, Scotland And Northern Ireland (No. 222)	£75
Rural Workers' Dwellings – Planning Control in the United Kingdom (2014) (No. 219)	£85
Commentary on the Valuation of Improvements under the Agricultural Tenancies Act 1995 (3rd Ed, 2014) (No. 217)	£50
An Agricultural Valuer's Guide to Residential Tenancies (Second edition) (2014) (No. 216)	£70
A Practitioner's Guide to Scottish Agricultural Rent Reviews (2013) (No. 215)	£80
Grazing Arrangements (Second edition) (2013) (No. 213)	£80
Entrepreneurs' Relief (2012) (No. 212)	£80
Guidance Notes on Agricultural Stock Valuations for Tax Purposes (2012) (No. 210)	£60
An Agricultural Valuer's Guide to Business Tenancies in England and Wales (2012) (No. 209)	£70
Heat from Renewable Sources (2011) (No. 208)	£70
Professional Fees in Compensation Claims (2011) (No. 206)	£20
Surrender and Regrant of Agricultural Tenancies: A Review of Issues (2011) (No. 205)	£75
Compensation for Revocation or Modification of Water Abstraction Licences (2011) (No. 204)	£50
The On-Farm Generation of Renewable Electricity (2011) (No. 203)	£100
Telecommunication Masts (2010) (No. 201)	£75
Valuation of Agricultural Tenancies (2009) (No. 197)	£25
The Powers of Utility Companies in Relation to Land (2009) (No. 195)	£25
Rent Reviews for Farm Business Tenancies (2008) (No. 191)	£25
Rent Reviews under the AHA 1986 (2008) (No. 190)	£25
Farming with Contractors (2007) (No. 188)	£25
Dilapidations on the End of a Tenancy (2007) (No. 187)	£25
Schedule of Time Limits (2006) (No. 185)	£25
Agricultural Tenancies (2006 Reforms and Update) (2006) (No. 184)	£25
Silage – A Valuer's Guide (2006) (No. 183)	£25
End of Tenancy Compensation under the Agricultural Holdings Act 1986 (2006) (No. 182)	£25
Preparing Farm Business Tenancies (1998) (No. 173)	£15
Notes for Probationers on Office Systems (2010)	£25
Guide to Costings of Agricultural Operations 2018	£20

Any of the above can be ordered via the website, www.caav.org.uk
or by contacting the CAAV office on 01452 831815.

The Central Association of Agricultural Valuers (CAAV) is the specialist professional body representing, briefing and qualifying some 2,900 professionals who advise and act on the very varied matters affecting rural and agricultural businesses and property in United Kingdom. Instructed by a wide range of clients, including farmers, owners, lenders, public authorities, conservation bodies and others, this work requires an understanding of practical issues and a professional approach which the CAAV brings to its advice to governments throughout the UK and in Brussels.